S0-AQI-913

The Rebel Trumpet

The Rebel Trumpet

by

GORDON D. SHIRREFFS

The Westminster Press
PHILADELPHIA

To Mary Kay Johnson, my adopted niece,
who, I am sure, will someday be a writer

LIBRARY OF CONGRESS CATALOG CARD NO. 60-9714

PRINTED IN THE UNITED STATES OF AMERICA

Chapter

I

Virginia,
July, 1861

THE ELEVENTH New York Volunteers, the Fire Zouaves, waited in the hot woods, listening to the steady, distant thudding of the artillery guns and to the irregular firing of musketry, which sounded like the popping of grease in a gigantic skillet. Beyond the dusty woods, across a high-banked and sluggish stream, the gun smoke hung close to the broken ground, mingled with the yellow dust churned up by wheels, hoofs, and marching feet.

The fighting had been going on for hours, but the Eleventh was not yet baptized by battle. The hot July sun and the dust of the Virginia roads had played havoc with the once bright uniforms of the Fire Zouaves. The red pants and caps, short blue jackets, and white gaiters had lost their freshness and all were now a neutral, dusty color, stained by sweat, but the heavy silken presentation flags at the center of the mass of waiting men were still bright, although they hung listlessly in the quiet air.

Lieutenant Colonel Farnham rode slowly along the line of his regiment of five hundred men. He looked almost nonchalant and cool as he rode, but anyone with half an eye could tell he was mentally gauging the Eleventh, wondering what would happen when they would be thrown into the battle that had swayed back and forth for hours, with the advantage first on one side and then on the other.

" Colonel, sir! When do *we* go in? " big Gershom Bates asked.

Farnham waved a hand. " Soon enough, my man," he said with a smile.

Bates whipped out a huge bowie knife and flourished it. " We'll go through them rebels like a greased pig at a lodge picnic! "

" That's the spirit, Bates! " Farnham called as he rode on.

Drummer Steven Ames, of *A* Company, shoved back his red, tasseled cap and wiped the sweat from his face. He looked down the line of his company. He wondered if they were all as scared as he was. The long march from Centreville had been hard enough on them, and Steve's drumming had aroused them at two o'clock that morning after a poor night's rest. Now it was late in the afternoon, and the battle that Bates had confidently predicted would be over in less than an hour had begun to stretch on and on, with no sign of the rebels running from the hard-fought field and with the firing increasing in volume.

" Worried, kid? " asked little gap-toothed Walt Mawson.

Steve shook his head. He looked down at his long legs in their baggy Zouave trousers and tight white leggings and wondered if they'd carry him to the fighting when the Eleventh's time came.

" That's where a cavalryman has it all over us infantrymen," said Walt philosophically. " We get scared and our legs give out, while a cavalryman's horse will always carry him along no matter how scared his rider is."

Gershom Bates swaggered up and down the line of *A* Company, eying the quiet and apprehensive men. " Why don't they send in us Fire Zouaves? " he bellowed.

Sergeant Mike Hogan shifted a little from where he rested with his back against a log. " Your time will come, me bucko," he said quietly.

Bates twisted his long mustachios. " It'd better, Sergeant! I'm not going back home to New York City without a bagful of rebels! "

" The war will last long enough for ye to get your fill."

Bates placed his hands on his hips and looked up and down the company line. " Not to my way of thinking," he said. " It will be a short war, Sergeant."

Most of the men nodded, as though they wanted to believe the big braggart.

" All wars are supposed to be short," said Hogan. He yawned. " They always are — at the beginning."

Bates eyed the noncom as though he was the very incarnation of pessimism. " I say this one won't last longer than this afternoon, that is, after the Eleventh gets at those rebels."

" Hear, hear," said Walt Mawson.

Hogan yawned again. " How many wars have ye been in, Bates? " he asked dryly.

Gershom Bates opened his wide mouth and then he shut it. Mike Hogan had trapped him there, for Bates had never heard a shot fired in anger, while Mike had fought in the British Army in India and had served with Garibaldi in Italy as one of " the thousand," the red-shirted patriots who had fought for Italian freedom in 1860. Bates swaggered off down the line, and Hogan grinned. " Now if Bates was a real veteran," he said to the men near him, " he'd be lying down resting instead of doing his fightin' with his big mouth."

Steve touched his dry lips with his tongue. He was dry, but water was scarce. He had placed a smooth pebble in his mouth to start the flow of saliva, a trick he had learned in the deserts of New Mexico and Mexico as a young boy. His canteen was about half full, whereas most of the green men about him had drained theirs dry long ago.

" Wish you was back in Mexico, kid? " asked Walt Mawson as he pulled off his left shoe and inspected a blister on his heel.

" *New* Mexico," said Steve.

Some of the men laughed nervously. It was a standing joke in *A* Company, which had started since that day in New York City when Steve had enlisted in the Eleventh as a drummer boy and had given outlandish New Mexico Territory as his home. New Mexico to most of the city-dwelling members of the regiment was away out back of beyond.

All through the hot and dusty woods men lay on their arms, listening to the muttering and smashing of battle across the sluggish stream that wound through the broken scrub timberland. The Eleventh New York Volunteers were part of Willcox's Brigade of Heintzelman's Third Division. The rest of the brigade was as green as the Eleventh — the Thirty-eighth New York, the First Michigan, and the Fourth Michigan. The only trained troops in the whole brigade were the regulars of Battery *D,* Second United States Artillery.

Walt Mawson stood up and peered through the smoky, dusty woods. " Some army we got," he said proudly. " Lookit all them men waiting like us to wipe out the rebels."

" 'Tisn't an army yit," said Sergeant Hogan. " 'Tis an armed mob, green as the hills of me native Killarney."

Some of the men looked angrily at the placid Irishman.

Steve stood up beside Walt Mawson. The woods were full of men, and here and there men drifted along, stopping to squat and talk with men of other regiments. They walked and talked and carried news from one unit to another, trying to fit the pieces of the puzzle together to get a clearer picture of the battle. In time, men like them would become the famed " newswalkers " of the Army of the Potomac and the Army of the Tennessee.

An armed mob, green as the hills of Killarney, thought Steve.

Raw as it was, the Union army was certainly colorful. Washington, D. C., had been filled with regiments from many states and in many different uniforms. There were volunteers and militia with a seasoning of smart regulars: the silk-stocking Seventh New York Volunteers, wearing their smart gray uniforms; the First Rhode Island Volunteers, wearing serviceable gray pants, dark-blue flannel shirts, slouch hats turned up at one side, and with long-haired Kady Brownell, wife of a sergeant, and his company's color-bearer; the fighting Irishmen of the Sixty-ninth New York Volunteers, with their bright emerald-green flag. Then there were the Seventy-ninth New York Volunteers, composed of Scots, many of whom wore tartan trousers and diced Glengarry caps, and the First New Hampshire Volunteers, who had appeared in Washington with sixteen baggage wagons, a brass band led by a drum major in a bearskin hat, a hospital wagon, and a contingent of nurses in gray traveling dresses and straw hats. There were other picturesque regiments, such as the Garibaldi Guards, the Thirty-ninth New York Volunteers, wearing jaunty red jackets and plumed *Bersaglieri* hats, a melting-pot regiment composed of Hungarians, Swiss, Germans, Italians, Frenchmen, and Spaniards, with a few Cossacks thrown in for good measure. There were at least four or five regiments of Germans in the army too, good soldiers whose commands were given in their native tongue.

"Lookit him!" cried out Walt Mawson.

Steve turned to see a mounted courier splashing across the stream with a folded dispatch in his mouth.

"What's the news?" yelled Gershom Bates.

The courier snatched the paper from his mouth. "Dispatch from General McDowell to Washington!" he called out. "We're winning! We've taken the Henry House plateau and have the rebels on the run!" Then he was gone through the woods, leaving a fleck of damp yellowish foam from the lathered horse on the back of Steven Ames's left hand.

"I told you so, Sergeant," crowed Bates to Hogan.

"The battle is not over yit."

“We’ll be in Richmond in a week! ” said Bates.

Most of the men were on their feet, with broad grins on their dusty, sweat-streaked faces.

“Too bad we didn’t get a chance to show them how the Fire Zouaves fight! ” thundered Gershom Bates.

Walt Mawson glanced sideways at Steve, with a shamed look on his face. “I ain’t sorry, Steve,” he said. He swallowed hard. “I guess I ain’t cut out to be a hero like Gershom Bates is.”

“He sure talks like one,” said Steve quietly.

“You ain’t as afraid as me, kid. You been shot at before, ain’t you? ” He looked closely at Steve. “By Apaches and Navahos and suchlike? ”

Steve nodded.

“In Mexico, wasn’t it? Makes a difference, don’t it? I mean, you’re used to it.”

Steve looked away as he tightened up the snares on his big field drum. “I don’t think anyone ever really gets used to it, Walt.”

Sergeant Hogan nodded. “Aye,” he said quietly.

Captain Michaels came down the line. “Play the long roll,” he said to Steve. “We’re moving up, drummer.”

Steve took his sticks from the brass drumstick carriage, which was hooked to the wide white-web drum sling. He took the drummer’s stance and began to beat the instrument. All through the woods, where Willcox’s Brigade had been waiting, other drummers took up the steady rolling.

There was a rattling and a clashing of equipment as the Eleventh New York fell in, dressed ranks, and then waited for the command to move out.

In a few minutes the regiment moved out of the hot woods into the still hotter Virginia sunshine, in a column of fours in double time.

The regimental commander and his aide splashed through the little stream, followed by the colors and by *A* Company, the color company. Here and there men dropped from the ranks to scoop up some of the sluggish water. " Watch it! " roared Sergeant Hogan. " Ye drink that swill and ye'll be no good to your country or to yourselves for the rest of the day! "

The water felt good on Steve's blistered feet as he slogged on at the head of the company with his drum hung across his shoulders by the trail ropes, bumping and banging against him. " What stream is this, sir? " he asked Captain Michaels.

The officer turned. " Bull Run," he said with a funny grin. " No one ever heard of it before and no one will ever hear of it again after this day."

They passed over a chopped-up area of land, stippled with dusty scrub trees, double-timing all the way. Now and then a man staggered from the ranks and fell over, sick from the heat and exertion.

" Close up! Close up! " yelled officers and noncoms.

They reached a road and followed it. Ahead of them, across the smoky fields, they saw a low plateau wreathed in battle smoke, on which perched a two-story house. Beside the house there were two Union batteries in roaring action, while on the far side of the hill, rebel guns answered back in defiance.

The Fire Zouaves came up from the Sudley Springs Road, with their rifles at right-shoulder shift, slogging toward the sound of the heaviest firing, with the bright colors slanted forward to lead them on, while behind the regiment was left a broad trail of exhausted men.

There was a continuous rattling of musketry from the right, while from the left came the steady thudding of the guns. Colonel Farnham drew in his horse and whipped out his sword to show his regiment the line to form upon. The tired men staggered into position and looked toward the enemy.

The two Union batteries were magnificent as they blasted flame and smoke, recoiled, were swabbed and loaded, aimed and fired again and again. The sweating, smoke-blackened gunners looked like demons from the nether regions as they served their roaring charges.

"Regulars those," said Captain Michaels as he mopped his red face. "Captain Griffin's Battery *D*, Fifth U. S. Artillery and Captain Ricketts' Battery *I*, of the First U. S. Artillery, the West Point Battery. They've been engaged hotly most of the day."

Steve felt his stomach roll a little in fear. He was tired and thirsty, and now fear had come to roost on his shoulders and keep him dreary company. A dead man lay in a hollow about fifty feet from the company, with clawed hands resting on the edge of the hollow as though he wanted to climb out and join the Zouaves. There were many other men scattered across the smoky fields like tumbled bundles of old clothing, and some of them were not good to look upon.

Steve glanced down the company line, and he knew most of the men were as scared as he was. But they were good material, formed by Colonel Elmer Ellsworth, of Chicago Zouave fame, from the rough and tough volunteer firemen of New York. Ellsworth himself had been slain by a hotel owner in Alexandria because he had taken a Confederate flag from the roof of the hotel, and his men of the Eleventh New York had sworn vengeance.

The roar of the battle seemed to increase, and there was a steady slapdash of musketry fire, while above it all the hoarse shouting of men and the frenzied screaming of wounded and frightened horses could be heard. On the far side of the plateau a line of men had formed in the shifting smoke, and the sun glinted on the bright bayonets as if on shards of broken mirror. They wavered in the heavy firing of the Union batteries.

"Why," said Walt Mawson in an odd, surprised voice, "them are rebels!" He swallowed hard. "They ain't running away neither, Stevie."

Gershom Bates stood a few feet ahead of his squad, with his rifle at present bayonet, and a fierce look on his mustachioed face. "Let 'em come on!" he cried.

Little Walt Mawson looked back down the slope. He edged away from his squad. " They's a wounded man down there," he said vaguely to no one in particular. " Maybe I'd better help him to the rear. Looks like a friend of mine from Hoboken."

Mike Hogan leaned casually on his rifle and glanced sideways at the little man. " Stay right where you are, Mawson," he said quietly.

" He'd better! " yelled Gershom Bates fiercely. " We want no cowards in the Fightin' Eleventh! "

Steve half closed his burning eyes. A memory had come back to him of the time his father's freighting wagons had been attacked by Mescalero Apaches on the dreaded Jornada del Muerto in New Mexico. Steve had been nine years old then, but he had known how to load rifles beside his mother and pass them on to the fighting teamsters.

There was a dull thud, and one of the Zouaves stepped from the ranks as though to get a better look at the enemy.

" Get back into ranks, Hillman! " yelled the captain.

Hillman turned a little, then fell heavily onto his back to look up at the sky with glazed eyes that did not see.

Steve's mother had died just as quickly, with a Mescalero arrow in her heart, right beside Steve in the wagon, that terrible day on the Jornada.

Steve opened his eyes wide, trying to drive the thought of death from his mind. The bursting shells looked like great swabs of cotton tinged with red and yellow, and there was death in every one of them.

It all seemed so vague and unreal, and there was a deep sickness in Steven Ames. Virginia was a long way from New Mexico, and yet he felt just then that they were one and the same in violence and death.

" You all right, Steve? " asked Walt in a shaky voice.

" Yes."

" You're a drummer," said Mike Hogan. " Go ye to the rear to help with the wounded."

" No," said Steve. In time of battle the orders of the

company commander were signaled by drum. Steve would be needed before long.

The whole Henry House plateau was a mass of struggling men. Riderless horses galloped through the melee, frantic in their terror.

" Stand fast, Zouaves! " called Captain Michaels.

The wavering line steadied.

Volley fire roared from a rebel brigade, and here and there Federal units began to drop back, slowly at first, and then a little faster. Some men pitched away their rifles, while others smashed them against rocks and trees. There was an odd feeling in the smoky air, the subtle turn of battle. No one could really say what it was, but it was there just the same. More and more of the Federals fell back and then some of them began to run. But there was no cessation of firing from the two Federal batteries led by Ricketts and Griffin; it seemed as though they planned to win the battle alone.

The smoke was thicker now, laced with sparkling red and yellow flashes. Captain Michaels went down on one knee and waved a hand back and forth in front of him as though to clear away the smoke for a better view of the battle.

" Saints preserve us! " yelled Sergeant Hogan. " Captain, sir, look ye to the right! "

Cavalry was forming near the fence line on Bald Hill, led by a big man with a flowing beard and a black ostrich plume in his slouch hat. The trotting cavalrymen obliqued from column to deploy into line, and then a trumpet seemed to shriek in joy, and even above the crash of battle the sound of the trumpet was like a silver bell, sending a thrill down the backbone of rebel and Federal alike.

Commands rippled down the ranks of the Eleventh New York, and the command wheeled to the right to face the charge with five hundred rifles. " Fire! " came the sharp command. The rifles flashed in a long, irregular volley of hazy bluish smoke laced by red flashes. Few of the Zouaves could see the effect of their volley because of the thick, drifting smoke, but the sound of that silvery trumpet carried through to them.

" Load! " commanded the company commanders.

" No! No! " yelled Mike Hogan. He thrust out his rifle at charge bayonet. " Meet them with the steel! "

It was too late to rectify the tactical error. The rebel troopers came through the smoke. Gershom Bates stared at the naked steel saber coming at him, threw down his rifle, and scampered down the hill, hurdling a fence while he yelled in fear. " We're whipped! Run for your lives! " His red cap blew off and revealed his shorn scalp.

" Stand fast, Zouaves! " called out little Walt Mawson. " Don't run! Meet them with the steel, lads! "

Steve stared at the little man. A knot of Zouaves, encouraged by Mawson's steady voice, stood fast with him to meet the roaring charge.

Then the cavalry struck the first of the waiting line, and it was chaos. Some of the men met the charge with the bayonet, while others stood staring stupidly at the troopers, with their ramrods still in their rifles and their jaws agape as they saw the great horses crash through the regiment. Some of the horses leaped at the yelling Zouaves as though they were clearing a fence, for few of them were trained cavalry horses but rather, hunters turned into war horses.

" Beat the rally! " yelled Hogan to Steve.

Steve raised his sticks and began to beat as hard as he could while the silver trumpet screamed above the sound.

" Run! " yelled a red-faced corporal.

" Stand fast! " cried Walt Mawson.

Steve played as he had never played before, but it was no use, for the Eleventh were breaking like reeds in front of the calvarymen. A horse struck Steve's drum and smashed it like a dropped pumpkin. Steve tried to get his silly little dress sword from its sheath. A fleeing Zouave knocked him down.

He saw Walt Mawson fighting like a tiger to get to him,

swinging his rifle by the barrel and yelling like mad. He reached Steve and gripped him by the collar to drag him to the safety of the stone fence a few feet away. "We'll hold them!" cried the little man.

The rebel trumpeter galloped past and his instrument flashed in the bright sunlight as he played the charge again and again, but the left side of his gray shell jacket was black with blood.

The Zouaves were hopelessly broken. The few of them who stood fast were knocked down or killed, and one of those who went down forever was little Walt Mawson, fighting to the last.

Steve got his back against the fence. "Stand fast!" he cried hoarsely.

"Look out, kid!"

The cry came from behind Steve. He turned to see a great bay horse falling down toward him while its hoofs lashed out and its rider fought to keep his seat. Then the hoofs descended and struck Steve on the left shoulder, driving him down beside the fence. The whole world seemed to dissolve into a chaotic, whirling pool of utter blackness, while through it all came the silvery voice of the rebel trumpet until that too faded away.

Chapter 2

Bull Run,
July, 1861

IT WAS DUSK when Steven Ames opened his eyes again. There was a vague recollection of hearing shooting and yelling and thudding of hoofs on the hard ground, mingled with periods of unconsciousness, and like everything else that hot, mad day, it seemed unreal, a nightmare.

He was pinned against the stone fence and above him was the dead bulk of the bay horse. Only the fact that Steve lay in a slight hollow at the lower edge of the fence had saved him from being crushed to death, but he could not get out from under the animal. He passed a shaking hand across his face, and it seemed swollen and crusted until he realized that what he felt was dried blood. His head throbbed as his field drum did when he played the long roll.

A strange, haunting sound came to Steve, and he knew it was the pitiful moaning of wounded and dying men, coming eerily through the dimness. He raised his head, wincing with the savage thrust of pain through it. His left side throbbed, but it didn't seem as though he had any broken bones.

He looked past the head of the horse. Here and there over the cluttered field of battle he saw moving pools of dim yellow light as men walked about with lanterns, looking for the wounded. Now and then they would kneel beside a body, then arise to thrust the bayoneted rifle into the ground close beside the body as a marker. Other men staggered up the slope, carrying wounded men on improvised litters formed of rifles and blankets. Steve narrowed his eyes. The uniforms looked alien to him, and he knew they were rebels. He craned his neck to look down toward the Sudley Springs Road. A column of men, followed by rolling guns, tramped along it, and as they passed a fire he saw the rebel flag at the head of the column.

He lay in a semideserted part of the field, although men passed back and forth not a hundred yards from him. Somewhere, out of his sight, a man was crying for his mother in a pitiful, racked voice.

Steve moved and felt the stones of the fence give a little, and he wondered grimly whether it had been his body, driven by the weight of the horse, that had loosened the stones. He shifted slightly, got one arm up, and began slowly to shove back the heavy stones until he could work his way out from under the horse.

The first body he saw was that of little Walt Mawson. His face was calm and peaceful-looking. Walt Mawson had died like a hero, fighting to the end in his first battle, while Gershom Bates had run off.

There wasn't any doubt now in Steve's mind that General McDowell had been soundly defeated. There was one thing he *did* know for sure, and that was that he had to get away from the battlefield or spend the rest of the war in a rebel prison. He was too used to the freedom of his home in New Mexico to live long in a filthy prison.

He unclasped his sword belt and dropped the ineffectual dress sword beside the shattered drum. Crawling along the fence line, he found a half-full canteen lying beside a dead rebel trooper. As he raised it to his lips he heard a faint, moaning cry from a clump of brush on the other side of the fence.

Steve stared into the dimness. Something was moving about beside a fallen horse. A head raised, and Steve knew he had been seen. " Watah! " the voice cried out, and there was a Southern intonation in it.

Steve stopped the canteen and drew out the knife he had brought from New Mexico with him, a parting gift from Hernán Calvillo, his boyhood friend in Santa Fe.

" Watah! " called the rebel again huskily.

Steve tested the edge of the keen knife with his thumb. If the fallen man raised an alarm when he saw the Zouave uniform on Steve, there would be little chance for Steve to escape, crippled as he was. Steve began to crawl along the fence line and the cold sweat broke out on his face from the pain of his side.

" Watah, comrade! "

Steve raised his head again. There were some litter bearers not a hundred yards away, and one of them had turned to listen to the sound of the wounded man's voice.

" What's wrong, Dan? " asked the other litter bearer.

" Heard a man calling for watah, Clay."

The other man laughed dryly. " They all are, Dannie." They walked on with their limp burden.

There were plenty of rebels close enough to hear the man if he made an outcry when he saw Steve, and yet Steve knew he could not let the man lie and suffer because of his terrible thirst. Steve held the canteen in one hand and the knife in the other, ready to use either one. He meant to escape from that battlefield, and no one was going to stop him!

He crouched beside the fallen horse and looked down at the rebel in the dimness. He was a slight man, smaller than Steve, and his groping hands were like those of a child. One of the hands gripped Steve's right wrist and gripped it tightly enough to make him wince. " Watah? " asked the man.

Steve nodded. He unstoppered the canteen with his teeth and held it toward the rebel. " Where are you hit? "

he asked before he placed it to the man's mouth.

There was a moment's hesitation. " Left side . . . high up . . . close to heart . . ."

" You can have water then."

The eyes seemed to bore through the dimness. *" You a Yankee? "*

Steve tightened his grip on the knife. It was a weapon he hated to use, although he had seen plenty of knifeplay at home.

" You heah me? " asked the man.

" What difference does it make? " asked Steve quietly. He held the canteen to the lips of the wounded man, crouching close beside him to stifle any outcry. It was then he realized that the rebel was hardly much older than he was.

The rebel finished drinking and rested his head against the horse beside him. " Poor Dandy," he said.

" Who? "

" My horse. Got a bayonet through the belly. But he kept agoing, Yank."

There was a faint light in the eastern sky. The moon was rising.

" Don't worry, Yank. I won't cry out."

There was something lying beside the wounded rebel. It shone dully in the darkness. It was a trumpet. Then Steve remembered the trumpeter who had gone past him at a gallop, putting his whole soul into his music with his left side shot to pieces.

" Who won? " asked the rebel.

" I'm not sure. But your people hold the battlefield."

" Then we did win! " There was no triumph in the voice.

" Yes," said Steve. He glanced back over his shoulder. They were still alone in their private section of the battlefield.

" Colonel Stuart said we would win. He knew."

" Colonel Stuart? "

The boy nodded, then winced in pain. " Colonel James Ewell Brown Stuart. Commander of the First Virginia Cavalry. We call him Jeb Stuart. It was us who smashed your line, Yank."

" I know," said Steve dryly.

The boy coughed. " We wavered a little when you *all* volleyed us, but the colonel called out to me. ' Dacey Curtis,' he yells, ' you play that there silver trumpet like you never did before.' And I did, Yank. . . ."

" I saw and heard you, reb."

Steve placed the canteen beside Dacey. " Good luck," he said. " I have to go now."

The hand gripped Steve's wrist with surprising strength. " No . . . you wait a bit . . ."

Steve placed his mouth close to Dacey's left ear. " Listen, rebel," he hissed. " Looks like I'm the only real live Yankee left on this battlefield, and I don't aim to sit around here waiting until they find me! I don't want to sit out the rest of the war in a reb prison eating corn pone, grits, and sow-belly! "

The boy smiled. " They ain't so bad, but I won't cry out, Yank."

Men moved about beyond the fence, looking for wounded. Steve lay low.

" Anyone ovah theah? " a man cried out.

Steve wet his lips and gripped his knife.

" Seems like we heard voices ovah theah! "

Dacey Curtis did not move or cry out, and the men moved slowly off.

" You're a fool," said Steve. " They might have saved you, Dacey. You're bad hit."

" I said I wouldn't cry out, Yank. I got something to tell you."

" It can wait."

Steve raised the knife, and the boy's eyes turned full upon him, but there was no fear in them.

Steve began to cut away the blood-stiffened material of

the gray shell jacket. The moon was starting to shed light on the field through low, ragged clouds. Steve looked closely at the wound and then he turned away, sickened by what he saw.

"No use, eh, Yank?"

Steve pulled the jacket over the wound.

"No use?" persisted the boy.

"You'll be all right."

"No . . . I know."

Steve wiped the sweat from the boy's face and then peeled off his own shell jacket. He rolled it and placed it under Dacey's head.

"Thanks, Yank."

"My name is Steve. Steven Ames."

"Steve, then. Where you from, Steve? They said you Frenchy-looking soldiers was from New York."

"That's right, but my home is in New Mexico."

Dacey coughed. "That's a long ways from heah."

"Yes. I've got to go now, rebel."

The boy raised his head. "Hand me thet trumpet, Yank."

Steve picked up the beautiful instrument and placed it in Dacey's dirty hands. The boy passed a caressing hand along it. "Pretty," he said softly. "Jeb Stuart said it would turn a coward into a hero when he heard it played right. 'Got magic in it,' my father said. He brought it from Mexico with him. Captured it in the wah we had down theah. Captured it from a Mexican lancer, but the trumpet had French words written on it."

"So?"

"My father always said it could do anything if you played it with heart."

Steve nodded. He could still remember the First Virginia Cavalry smashing into the ranks of the Fire Zouaves and of how the silver trumpet, played by a mortally wounded boy, had spurred on the cavalry.

The moon was now shining on the low hills. If Steve

was to make good his escape, he'd have to leave right away.

" I know you have to go, Steve," said Dacey.

" Yes."

The dirty hands passed up and down the trumpet. " This shouldn't be lost, Steve."

" It will be found with you, Dacey."

" No. It has to be passed from one soldier to another, Steve."

Steve stared curiously at the boy.

" My father got it from the trumpeter of the Mexican lancers that way. On his death bed my father gave it to my brothah James. Brother James died of camp fever at Harper's Ferry and left the trumpet to me. He was trumpeter for Jeb Stuart, and I stayed on to fill his place."

" I've got to go, Dacey," said Steve desperately.

" In a minute, Steve." Dacey raised his head and placed the trumpet in Steve's hands. " Take care of it," he said thickly.

" But I'm a Yank, Dacey! "

The eyes opened wide. " Don't matter none. This war is madness anyway. That's what my mothah said when I left for Harper's Ferry to get the trumpet. Fathah against son and brothah against brothah. Today you and me fought against each othah and tonight you tried to help me. Take the silver trumpet, Steve. Don't use it against us rebels. Try to use it to help each othah. I don't know how, but I know you'll find a way." The head raised, and the blue eyes were fierce in the moonlight. " But if you use it wrong, you'll pay for it, if I have to come back from the grave."

" Take it easy, Dacey."

" That trumpet has been to too many wahs. 'Bout time a beautiful thing like thet was used for good instead of evil."

The beautiful instrument felt cool and alive in Steve's hands.

Dacey Curtis rested his head on the shell jacket. " Good-by, Steven Ames," he said quietly.

Steve stood up. " I'll go and get one of your doctors."

" They'll take you prisoner."

" It doesn't matter."

The boy smiled. " You see? The trumpet is already working its magic on you, Steve."

Steve opened his mouth and then shut it. The moon shone on the boy's face. His eyes were wide open, but they did not see, and there was a calm smile on the still, pale face.

" Good-by, Dacey Curtis," said Steve. He slung the silver trumpet over his shoulder by the yellow silken cord and then walked to the north toward the thick woods, and he did not look back as he walked, but the moonlight reflected from the polished surface of the trumpet.

On the Henry House plateau a tall, bearded man looked down on the battlefield. " What's that shining in the moonlight, Hastings? " he demanded of an officer beside him.

The officer stared. " Nothing, sir."

" Might be an escaping Yankee."

The officer smiled. " There isn't a Yankee left on this field, sir, who isn't dead, wounded, or a prisoner of war."

" All the same, there's something moving down there."

" Moonbeams, sir, nothing but moonbeams. The moonbeams of victory for the Confederacy."

" Yes, I think you're right." Colonel Jeb Stuart kneed his horse away from the fence and rode toward the campfires of the victorious Southern army.

Chapter

3

Washington, D. C.,
August, 1861

T*HE BROILING* August sun was beating down upon the tent, forming curiously mottled patterns on the dirt floor. There was scarcely a breath of wind, and when the wind did blow a little, it brought with it the stench of the nearby Tiber Canal where the decaying offal of the government slaughterhouses floated in the filthy waters.

Hoarse commands came to Steven Ames as he lay in his tent. *A* Company was out on the hard-packed drill field not far from the company street, going through the motions and times of loading and firing under the whiplash voice of Sergeant Michael Hogan.

The fever Steve had contracted on his long march through the night rain from the field of Bull Run had finally laid him low, and he was not the only one. Twenty per cent of the company was ill with fever in the filthy tents. Five times in the past two days the burial wagon had passed down the company street. If it kept up, the Fire Zouaves would lose more men in the camp than they had at Bull Run.

Steve felt under his sagging cot for his canteen. He sipped a little of the warm water and then wet his hand to cool his burning forehead. As he placed the canteen back

on the floor, his hand touched the canvas-wrapped silver trumpet that he had brought from the battlefield. It had been stolen once by a man from *B* Company and recovered by Sergeant Hogan while Steve had been delirious with fever. Sergeant Hogan had said it would bring a fine price in a Washington hock shop.

Steve closed his eyes. He could still see the drawn face of Dacey Curtis. Two weeks had gone by since the battle, and the Federal troops had fallen back to defend Washington. The rebel papers were screaming that it had been total defeat, that the North was whipped, that one Southerner could whip a dozen Northerners, and so on and so on. Washington itself was full of Southern sympathizers, many of whom had stood on street corners in the drizzling rain, smirking as they saw the dispirited Federal troops straggle back into the city.

A drum thudded lifelessly in the hot, still air. A detail of cavalrymen trotted past the Zouave camp, sending yellow dust swirling into the tents.

Steve coughed and sat up, holding his head in his hands. The tent seemed to tilt and whirl, and there was a deadly fear within him that he, too, would end up in the growing graveyard just beyond the camp. Suddenly, with all his heart and soul, he wished he was back in the cool, clear air of his native New Mexico, and he knew he was homesick. These people were not really his people. Some of them he liked, such as Sergeant Hogan and Captain Michaels, and he missed his friend Walt Mawson, who had died at Bull Run.

A shadow fell across the floor of the tent, and Steve looked up to see a young officer, wearing the bare shoulder straps of a second lieutenant, smiling at him. Steve got to his feet and managed a passable salute.

"Sit down, Steve," the officer said.

Steve sat down gratefully. "How did you know my name, sir?"

The officer looked about the littered tent. "Volunteers

all right. Regulars would never leave a tent looking like this."

Steve felt a little angry, but the officer's smile disarmed him. " It takes a little time to train men, sir."

The officer nodded. He sat down on a cot and placed his sword between his knees. He rested his hands on the sword and studied Steve. " How do you feel? "

" All right, I guess."

" You don't look like it, Steve."

Steve shook his head. " I guess all of us will have to go through a bout of fever sooner or later."

" I hope not. I'm Lieutenant Lloyd Bruce, Third United States Cavalry."

" Pleased to meet you, sir." Steve eyed the officer. The Third was well known to him, for they garrisoned posts throughout New Mexico, and as far as he knew, they were still stationed in the territory. " The Mounted Rifles," he said.

Bruce smiled. " I see you know the *old* name."

" Yes, sir. The Brave Rifles."

" I came here to look you up, Steve. I'm glad I did. This is no place for you."

" It's *my* regiment, Lieutenant."

The dark eyes studied Steve. " Is it? New York Volunteer Firemen. Toughs and roughs from the tenements. Why did you enlist in the Eleventh? "

Steve shrugged. " I was in school, and it was spring. The bands played and the flags waved, and then the President called for volunteers. I knew how to play a drum. The rest was easy."

" I would probably have done the same thing. Well, gather your gear together. You're coming with me."

" I don't understand, sir."

Lieutenant Bruce reached inside his blouse and brought out some papers. He held one of them up between two fingers. " This is your honorable discharge from the Eleventh New York Volunteers."

" But, sir. . . ! "

Bruce took up another paper. " Wait! This is your enlistment in the First New Mexico Volunteer Infantry, now stationed near Santa Fe, Territory of New Mexico."

Steve stared at Bruce. " You're moving too fast for me, sir. Maybe it's the fever. Maybe you don't exist at all."

" You can pinch me — that is, except that it isn't exactly military courtesy to do so."

" But why am I to leave the Eleventh? " Steve stood up. " I did my duty! I was knocked unconscious on the field and came back to my regiment when I was able to do so! That's more than many of them did. Gershom Bates ran away when the cavalry charged us, and we haven't seen him since! "

" You don't understand. How old are you, Steve? "

" Eighteen, sir! "

Bruce thrust a tongue against the inside of his cheek. " You might be. You're big enough. But . . ."

" Seventeen, then! "

Bruce rubbed a hand against his jaw.

Steve wet his lips. " Sixteen? " he asked in a small voice.

" Fifteen, Steve. I know for a fact."

" What happens now? "

" There are plenty of fifteen-year-old lads in the army. Yes, and younger lads than that too, but it is required for them to have their parent's consent for enlistment."

Steve's eyes narrowed.

Bruce went on. " I've heard you are a good field drummer, Steve. Learned to play from old Sergeant Honus Schuster, retired, of the Seventh United States Infantry. Am I right? "

" Yes, sir." The officer knew far too much, thought Steve.

" Sergeant Hogan says you are the best field drummer in the Eleventh."

Things were beginning to fit together now.

" The fact is, Steve, you did not have your father's consent to join the volunteers. Therefore, you have committed fraudulent enlistment. Your father wrote to your schoolmaster, who in turn located you in the Eleventh New York. He passed on that information to your father, who at that time was in Independence, Missouri, ready to leave on the Santa Fe Trail with a Government wagon train under his charge. I can assure you that there was some mighty fast action after that.

" Your father wrote to Senator Chavez in Washington. The senator contacted the War Department. There's no need of my telling you how much weight your father and uncle can pull in Government matters when they wish to."

Steve nodded. " Yes," he said dryly.

Bruce held up the papers. " Therefore, it was easy to get your discharge from the Eleventh and have the papers made out for your enlistment in the First New Mexico. This time, with your father's permission."

" I won't leave the Eleventh, sir."

Bruce stood up, and his eyes hardened. " You're wanted home in New Mexico, Steve."

" I won't run away like a whipped pup! "

" Attention, Drummer Ames! "

Steve stiffened.

" Now listen to me, soldier! I've gone through a lot of trouble to get these papers cleared and to find you! I haven't much time left in Washington, and I don't intend to waste it arguing with you! "

" But, sir, Sergeant Hogan says this will be a long war, that every man is needed. We haven't been licked yet, sir. One battle doesn't win a war."

" I agree with you, Ames."

" That's why I want to stay here rather than go to New Mexico and sit in a garrison for the rest of the war."

Bruce came closer to Steve. " I can see you know little of what has been going on in the rest of the country while you've been serving here. There will be plenty for all of us to do in New Mexico."

Steve couldn't help smiling. " What does New Mexico

have to do with the war, sir? Away out back of beyond. The lost colony of the United States."

"The last information I have is that Texas Mounted Rifles are on the move from San Antonio toward El Paso del Norte. It's also rumored that a column of Texas rebels plan to invade New Mexico."

Steve grinned. "Some rumor. What would they gain by that, sir?"

"Would you believe me if I told you that Luke Comfort learned that information?"

The grin faded away. "The best scout in the Southwest! I've never heard of him bringing in any wrong information."

Bruce nodded. "I have orders to join the Third Cavalry in the District of New Mexico as soon as possible, carrying important secret dispatches from the War Department to Colonel E. R. S. Canby, district commander. Your father requested that you accompany me. By a little manipulation, it was arranged that you get discharged from the Eleventh, enlisted in the First, then go with me as my orderly to Santa Fe."

Things were moving too fast for Steve. He passed a hand across his burning forehead.

"As of right now, Drummer Stevens Ames, you are on detached duty from the First New Mexico Volunteers, District of New Mexico, to act as mounted orderly to Second Lieutenant Lloyd Bruce, Third United States Cavalry, District of New Mexico, courier from the War Department, Washington, D. C., to Santa Fe, Territory of New Mexico, via Independence, Missouri, and the Santa Fe Trail."

Steve couldn't help laughing at the mock-solemn air with which the young officer had made his speech, and he knew he would grow to like Lieutenant Bruce very much on the long and arduous trip to Santa Fe.

Bruce placed Steve's enlistment paper in the First New Mexico on top of the boy's cased drum and then he looked steadily at Steve. Steve took a pen and a bottle of ink from Corporal Duffy's foot locker. He squatted down beside the drum and signed the paper, then watched while Lieutenant Bruce signed it. Bruce then administered the oath to Steve.

Steve looked about the hot tent. He'd miss the members of his mess.

" Are you well enough to travel now? " asked the officer. " I have two horses waiting for us at the head of the company street."

" I can ride, sir. I can *always* ride."

" That's what I've heard. Like a centaur, Senator Chavez said. You should be in the cavalry, Steve."

Steve flushed.

" Get your gear together," said Bruce.

Steve picked up his haversack and put his personal things into it. He picked up the silver trumpet and then looked at his new field drum, which had replaced the one lost at Bull Run.

" Is that all you have? " asked Bruce.

" Yes, sir."

" We'll have to get you out of that Zouave uniform and into regulation blues."

Steve looked quickly at him.

" No offense, Steve, to you and the gallant Fire Zouaves, but you'd look a little silly chasing Kiowas near Plum Buttes in that getup."

Steve nodded. " It is a little gay for that purpose, sir."

A hoarse command sounded at the head of the company street. Feet thudded against the hard ground in the unmistakable rhythm of marching men. Steve walked to the door of the tent. *A* Company came down the street, rifles at right-shoulder shift. More commands rattled out, and the company swung from column to company front and grounded arms. The dust floated over the line of tents.

" Smartly done," said Bruce.

" Dismissed! " roared Sergeant Hogan. He wiped the sweat from his face and then came toward Steve and the officer. He saluted. " 'Tis hot work, but it has to be done before we can best the rebels at their own game, sir." He eyed Steve. " So ye're leavin' the regiment? "

" Yes, Sergeant. As though you didn't know."

Hogan avoided Steve's hard stare. " Well, 'tis for the best, me boy. This is no place for ye. Go home to New Mexico Territory. From what the lootenant has told me, thayer might be a bit of a fight back thayer too."

" Oh, sure, sure," said Steve dryly.

" Don't *ye* be too sure thayer won't be! Ye wait! 'Twill be a long war and a hard one! Ye know that country and ye know them people. 'Tis me honest belief they can use ye thayer and that ye'll get a bellyful of fightin' before ye are much older."

The men of the company stood about leaning on their rifles instead of going to their tents. Steve turned to the officer. " I'd like to say good-by to my messmates, sir."

" I expect you to."

Steve walked to the company and shook hands all around.

" We'll sure miss your lively drumming," said big Sam Donalds.

" Except at reveille," said grinning Orton Rybal.

" The best of luck to ye, Stevie," said Corporal Duffy.

It was hard to look at the smiling faces. Steve waved a hand and went back to the officer and Hogan.

" Now, mind ye, Steve," said the sergeant, " ye have the makings of a good soldier in ye. Remember what I taught ye! "

" How can I forget? "

" Repeat the soldier's catechism once more for me! "

Steve snapped to attention. " Keep my eyes open and my mouth shut; be first in the mess line and in the pay line; never volunteer for anything under any circumstances! "

Hogan nodded in deep satisfaction. " Aye, ye'll do, son." He looked at the trumpet. " Ye'll take that along, no doubt? "

" Yes."

" A strange story about that. Somehow I have a feeling that thayer is magic in that horn. 'Tis the Irish in me, no doubt."

" No doubt," said Bruce with a smile.

Steve squeezed the trumpet. It has to be given from one soldier to another, Dacey Curtis had said.

" A beautiful instrument," said Hogan.

Take the silver trumpet, Steve, the dying boy had said. Don't use it against us rebels. Try to use it to help each other. I don't know how, but I know you'll find a way.

" We'll have to leave," said Lieutenant Bruce. " We can get a train out of here in three hours. Time enough to get you outfitted, Steve."

Steve held out his hand to Sergeant Hogan. Hogan took it in his ham of a hand. " Good luck, me boy. May the wind be always at your back and a light in your path."

" A fine Irish thought," said Bruce.

Hogan's eyes were suspiciously bright. " No. 'Twas Robbie Burns said that."

The two of them walked along the dusty company street. As far as the eye could see, there were tents in the fields and on the hills, while the sun flashed on brightly scoured shovels as earthworks were being dug to defend Washington. There was a steady, low murmuring of many voices. The sun also shone on brass gun barrels and on the bayonets of the pacing sentries. Drumbeats and bugle calls came on the warm wind.

" You'll never forget this place," said Bruce.

" No, sir."

" Some memories have a way of staying with us."

" Yes, sir."

The officer clapped Steve on the back. " But you'll be glad to have a horse beneath you and to feel the dry prairie wind against your face."

Steve smiled. He could almost feel that clean, dry wind

now, sweeping across miles and miles of plains to the land of New Mexico, where wolf-fanged mountains stood etched against an incredibly blue sky dotted with cotton-puff clouds sailing steadily along. It would be good to go home.

Chapter 4

Glorieta Pass, New Mexico Territory, September, 1861

A *SHAFT* of lightning flashed across the sullen sky and seemed to lance into the huge, somber bulk of El Pilone. For an instant, the eerie light revealed the rugged walls of the deep canyon, stippled with shaggy piñon and juniper trees, and then the canyon was in darkness again. There was a distant thudding of the drums of the Thunder People in the gorges.

Lieutenant Lloyd Bruce turned in his saddle, resting a hand on his cantle pack.

Steven Ames turned too. "What's wrong, sir?"

"How far are we from Santa Fe now?" asked Bruce.

"About eighteen miles."

"I wish we had stayed at Koslowski's Ranch, as they asked us to."

The night was dark again. The two horses followed the dim road at the bottom of the deep pass. Steve swung his single-shot Sharps carbine from where it was slung at his side, so that it rested across his thighs. A heavy navy cap-and-ball Colt pistol was holstered at his right side.

Steve's dun tossed its head. "What is it, Zouave?" asked Steve quietly. The mount had been waiting for him at Independence, a gift left for him there by his father, and there was no mistaking his father's fine hand in picking out horseflesh.

"They said Jicarilla Apaches had been troublesome in here the past few months," said Bruce.

"They won't attack two well-armed soldiers, sir."

"Don't be so cool about this!"

Steve grinned a little in the darkness. "We've come eight hundred miles across hostile Indian country with nothing happening. Nothing will happen this close to the end of our trip, sir."

Bruce waved a hand. "Don't be too sure about that!"

There was a spit of rain in the night air. Steve looked up at the dark sky as a faint web of lightning traced a course across it. Bruce had been in a hurry ever since they had left the wagon train behind them at Las Vegas, in New Mexico, to push on ahead to Santa Fe. They had been safe enough on the long trail from Independence. Few Indian tribes would attack a well-armed caravan unless they had overwhelming numbers. They had received too many bloody noses from fooling around with the tough caravaneers.

The wind keened up the canyon. Steve shivered a little despite the warmth of his thick issue blouse. He had been completely outfitted in Washington before he had left there — dark-blue blouse, light-blue trousers, a forage cap with the infantry trumpet insignia on it, which he had personally made sure was just a mite too small so that he could perch it jauntily on one side of his head as he had seen the Regulars do.

"Wait!" said Bruce.

They drew rein and sat their horses in the darkness, listening to the moaning wind. It was a familiar place to Steve, for he had often traveled through there with his father's freighting trains. But tonight it seemed different, a strange alien difference that began to bother him.

"Jicarillas won't attack at night, sir," said Steve.

"I've heard that one before."

" Their souls will wander forever in darkness if they are killed at night."

Bruce passed a hand along the barrel of his carbine and then touched the locked dispatch case that was slung at his side and that never left him, awake or asleep. " They said I was to proceed as fast as possible to Santa Fe," he said, almost as though he was talking to himself. " Hurry! Hurry! Hurry! "

Steve eyed the young officer. Lieutenant Bruce had undergone quite a change since he had left Las Vegas and the importance of the dispatches had unnerved him more than Steve had realized.

" They said there were *ladrones* in here too," said Bruce.

Steve nodded. " There always are thieves in here, sir." He patted his carbine. " Few of them have the nerve to attack soldiers though, sir. They like the odds with them."

" Perhaps."

The officer looked back down the canyon. " I think we had better hole up until dawn."

" That's a favorite attacking time for the Jicarillas, sir."

Bruce cut a hand sideways to quiet Steve. The officer was brave and intelligent, but it hadn't taken Steve long to find out that he knew next to nothing about hostile Indians. Another thing Steve had learned was that Bruce didn't like to be reminded about his ignorance of Indians. He knew Steve had been raised in frontier country among skilled Indian fighters and scouts, such as his own father, and the knowledge of that had seemed to irritate the officer.

Steve couldn't help himself. " It's better to travel at night in Indian country and hole up by day, sir," he said.

" I'm in command here! We can't see to shoot in this murk! "

" They won't — "

" Be quiet, soldier! I've heard enough of your expert opinions! Is there any place along here where we can get shelter from the coming rain? "

" Half a mile up the road, Lieutenant, there's a place where a rock overhang would provide shelter. There's a spring there too, and grazing for the horses. It's a favorite camping place of my father's."

" Good! "

The rain was pattering down on the dry leaves when Steve led the way from the rutted road toward the dim bulk of the great rock overhang to the south. Steve swung down and took the reins of both horses as Lieutenant Bruce peered about. " This looks just fine, Steve," he said.

Steve nodded. It would be a long, hard wait for him until dawn. He didn't like the idea at all, but there was nothing he could do about it but sweat it out until they got on the road again.

Bruce was still nervous. He prowled back and forth as Steve took his gum-rubber talma from his saddlebag and put it on. " This is a long way from the war," growled the officer.

Steve led the horses to the shelter and leaned against Zouave, listening to the steady pattering of the rain. The very air seemed full of the electrical odor of the lightning discharges and the fresh smell of the rain, but there was something else in the air too — the odor of fear.

Bruce put on his talma and walked to the far end of the rock overhang with his carbine in his hands. Steve eyed him idly in the faint light from the flashes high overhead. Suddenly Steve stiffened. Something had seemed to move in the darkness beyond the officer.

Steve walked toward Bruce. " Maybe we had better go on, sir," he suggested.

Bruce shook his head, then walked farther out from the rock. It was then that Steve saw the sudden movement in the brush and he opened his mouth to yell, but it was too late.

The warrior seemed to appear from nowhere, with raised knife in his hand, and even as Steve darted forward he saw the knife dart down against the back of Lieutenant

Bruce. The officer grunted and went down on one knee, and his carbine fell from his limp hands.

Something grated on the rocks behind Steve. He whirled and instinctively cocked and raised his carbine. There was no time to aim at the racing Jicarilla. Steve fired and knew he had hit the warrior, for he staggered back and fell heavily.

Steve turned again, just as a brilliant lance of lightning shot down the pass, to see the first warrior crouching beside the officer, slashing away at the strap that held the dispatch case at Bruce's side.

There was no time to reload the carbine or draw pistol. Steve remembered his Zouave training. He darted forward, reversed the carbine, and drove the steel-shod butt hard against the head of the warrior. The warrior looked up with wide eyes and then fell beside the officer. There was no time to lose. Steve had been told time and time again by Lieutenant Bruce that nothing mattered except getting those dispatches to Santa Fe, despite anything that might happen to him.

Steve snatched up the dispatch case and ran toward his dun. He swung up onto the horse and slapped him with the carbine barrel. Using his spurs, he galloped toward the road. He glanced back as he rode, and in the cold illumination of the lightning he saw the set face of Lloyd Bruce and knew that he was dead.

Three warriors seemed to rise from the very ground as Steve reached the edge of the road. They raised their weapons, but Steve sank the steel into the flanks of the dun and the big horse smashed into the three warriors, scattering them like chaff. "*¡Madre de Dios!*" one of them screamed as he went down.

A gun flashed behind Steve as he bent low and lashed Zouave on down the road, and it seemed to him as though the slug picked at his left sleeve. He raced to the west as the rain came down in a slashing downpour.

Steve rounded a huge rock shoulder and then reloaded

as he let the dun ease off a little. It was still a long way to Santa Fe.

He looked back, although there was nothing to see. He had grown to admire and respect Lieutenant Lloyd Bruce during the long journey from Washington. The officer had fulfilled his duty but had died almost in sight of his goal, and it was up to Steve to finish the mission.

The road was empty. There was a cold feeling within Steve, for there had been something wrong about those Jicarillas back there. In the swift and deadly flurry of action there had been little time to think, but now the reaction set in and he felt sick. They *never* attacked at night.

The dispatch case bumped against his side, and he cast away his sickness. This was war. A man made comrades and lost them quickly in time of war. One way or another, by separation or by death, comrades left and were never seen again, but a man's duty stayed with him always. Those dispatches must get to Santa Fe, and Steven Ames, of the First New Mexico Volunteer Infantry, was the one who had to get them there.

Chapter

5

Santa Fe, New Mexico Territory,
September, 1861

THE RAIN was still falling when Steve Ames reached the first adobe houses of Santa Fe. There was a faint tinge of the false dawn in the eastern sky. The houses seemed to squat despondently in the wet, with their brightly painted doors and small, secretive windows, while from the flat roofs muddy water poured out of the spouts, forcing Steve to ride in the center of the narrow, winding street.

There was little joy in him at his home-coming. When he had first left Washington with Lieutenant Bruce he had still been a little bitter about leaving his friends in the Eleventh New York. Then he had grown to accept the idea of returning home, and gradually he had learned that he had really wanted to return home all the time. But now it seemed as though he had left part of himself back there in lonely Glorieta Pass with Lieutenant Bruce, as he had also left a part of himself at Bull Run with Walt Mawson and Dacey Curtis.

He skirted a rushing irrigation ditch, then rode toward San Francisco Street and followed it to the wide deserted plaza with the long bulk of the Governor's Palace dominating the northern side. Beyond the plaza he rode toward the narrow street where his father's house was. The cold, wet wind moaned ceaselessly through the cottonwoods and willows.

He turned into the street and looked eagerly down it. It hadn't changed a bit in the two years he had been away. He remembered the day he had left there in a stiff, store-bought suit, bound for the Santa Fe Trail, to end up eventually at Albright's Academy for Boys and Young Gentlemen in New York City.

He dismounted in front of the great door that had been cut into the thick adobe walls to permit carriages to pass through into the patio. It was studded with square-hewn bolts and heavy metal fittings. He tried the handle of the smaller door that was let into the big one, although he knew well enough it would be locked. *Ladrones* prowled the streets of Santa Fe at night looking for every opportunity.

Steve took off his cumbersome talma and then walked down the side lane to where a great tree hung a thick branch over the wall. He had climbed that tree many a time, both to get in and to get out of the house, without his father's permission of course. He gripped the branch and swung up his legs to get a toe hold in the niche that had eroded itself into the adobe wall. It was a matter of seconds to pull himself along the wall, then drop lightly atop the roof of a storehouse. He walked to the edge and let himself down into the wide, flagged patio.

The great house was built in the form of a rough square, with rooms on the west and east sides, the great hall on the north side, and stables and storage rooms on the south side. The patio had been his mother's kingdom in the old days, where she had tended her flowers and shrubs, had fed the birds and squirrels, and had done her sewing.

There wasn't a light on in the house. He crossed the puddled patio and opened the door that was the inner entry into the patio, then passed through the dark passageway to the outer door. He lifted the heavy bar from its metal supporting arms and eased back the huge door. Then he led Zouave into the patio and to the stables.

It was dawn when he came out of the stable. He carried his gear into the little hallway that led into the long, low living room. He lighted a Rochester lamp on the old Spanish Colonial table and then paused to look about himself. The room had not been changed.

The lamplight glistened from the top of his mother's rosewood piano, which had been brought at great expense over the Santa Fe Trail. His father's polished Hawken rifle was missing from the wooden pegs over the beehive fireplace, and he knew then that his father was not at home.

Steve took off his wet forage cap and damp blouse and hung them on a chair while he looked about the familiar room. Piñon wood was stacked vertically in the fireplace, and he took flint and steel and struck a light. The dry wood crackled sharply, and he warmed his hands at it.

"Does the house look any different, Steve?" the quiet voice said.

Steve jumped a little, then turned to see his uncle standing in the doorway that led to the bedrooms. Carter Ames was a tall, bearded man, a good many years older than Mark Ames, Steve's father. His eyes were gray, and there were times when there was a fierce light in them, for Carter Ames was a fighter. Steve stood up as his uncle came to him, then drew him close in a bear hug. "You look more like your father every day," he said, "but there is a strong touch of your mother in you too."

"Where is Father?"

"Down south. On territorial business. Your father acts like a man obsessed since this war started. He's trying to hold New Mexico for the Union all by himself, it seems."

Steve nodded. He might have known that.

"You've grown a lot and filled out, Steve. You'll soon be as big as your father."

Carter Ames sat down and studied Steve. "How was the battle, Steve?"

" Pretty bad, Uncle."

" They all are. It was a foolish thing for you to do."

" There were a lot of boys younger than myself there."

Carter Ames nodded. " Yes. I would think so. Where is Lieutenant Bruce? "

Steve looked away.

" What's wrong, boy? "

Steve turned. " Lieutenant Bruce was killed by Jicarillas late last night in Glorieta Pass."

Carter Ames leaped to his feet. " Good heavens! The dispatches! "

Steve walked to the hallway and got the wet leather case. He handed it to his uncle. " I managed to get away from the Jicarillas with them, sir."

" What happened? "

Steve quietly told the story.

" You've got courage, boy," said his uncle. " Thank God you came through safely yourself."

Steve fingered the bullet hole he had found in his left sleeve. " I was lucky it was so dark and that they weren't mounted."

" I cannot imagine why they'd attack at night." Carter Ames touched the dispatch case. " Bruce knew how important these dispatches were. He was a fool to come through that pass with just a boy as escort. No offense to you, Steve, for you played the part of a man. Thank heaven you were there! "

" I knew they were important, sir."

" You have no idea how important, son."

Steve warmed his hands at the fire. The thought of the tight little fight in the pass had chilled him. " I'm not so sure they were Jicarillas though, sir."

The gray eyes half closed. " No? Why not? "

" First, you know they don't like to fight at night."

" Yes."

" Then when I knocked down the warrior who had killed Lieutenant Bruce the lightning flashed and I got a good look at him."

" So? "

" His eyes were light, sir. And he had blond hair. The whole incident was odd. Jicarillas attacking at night. A warrior with fair hair. Then, when the warrior had downed Lieutenant Bruce he didn't snatch at his weapons as most Apaches would do, for you know how they value fine weapons, but instead he grabbed for the dispatch case."

" Yes," his uncle said softly.

" When I broke for the road, Zouave crashed into three more of them and one of them cried out in Spanish as he went down."

" Zouave? "

" My horse, sir."

" I see." Carter Ames looked into the crackling fire.

" Perhaps they were *ladrones* disguised as warriors, sir."

" No . . . I do not think so, Steve. You know little of what has been going on here. Someone knew that those dispatches were coming through Glorieta Pass in the hands of Lieutenant Bruce. There are forces working here in New Mexico determined to turn the territory over to the Confederacy. There are other forces, just as determined, who work to save New Mexico for the Union. True, many people in the East think this territory is hardly worth bothering about, but they are blind fools! "

" What do you mean by that, sir? "

" I'll tell you when we have eaten. Get out of those wet clothes. I think there must be some of your old clothing in your room. I'll have time to whip up some grub for us while you're changing. It wouldn't do for Colonel Canby to see you in a messy uniform and with an empty belly."

Steve walked to his room at the far end of the hallway. It was just the same as it had been the day he had closed the door on it two years ago — the whitewashed walls, neatly hung with calico sheeting on the lower four feet to keep the whitewash from rubbing off on one's clothing; the crudely carved bedstead with the thick woolen trade blankets on it; even the little carved *santo* stared woodenly at him from its niche in the wall. The Ames were not

Catholics, but they lived in a predominantly Catholic community, and Steve had become accustomed to their ways. Old Rosa Abeyta had worked in the house after his mother had died, and she had placed the *santo* in the niche to stand guard over Steve while he slept.

He took some of his old trail clothing from the great wooden wardrobe. Though they had fitted him rather loosely two years ago, now he had a hard squeeze getting into them, but they were warm and dry. He carried his damp clothing into the living room and hung it near the fire.

In a little while his uncle came into the room from the kitchen, bearing a heavily laden tray. Carter Ames smiled. " Warmed-over frijoles and hard bread. All I have left from last night. I don't eat here very often now that we have no housekeeper. Rosa married again and lives south of here with her new husband, Eusebio Campos, the muleteer. I haven't been able to get a decent housekeeper since then."

" Smells good to me."

Carter Ames placed a pot of chocolate near the fire to warm. Steve noted that the dispatch case hung from the old man's wide belt and that the butt of a pistol showed from his pocket. He was a well-known lawyer in the territory and had sat as a judge in territorial courts. He was a powerful factor in the land and a courageous man, but above all else he was a Union man, and as long as men like Carter Ames would fight for New Mexico Territory, the Confederacy might get a rough comeuppance. Of that, Steve was quite sure.

Carter Ames shoved back his plate and then walked to the fire. He placed more piñon wood on it and warmed his big hands at the cheery blaze. He spoke over his shoulder to Steve. " Times are troublous here, Steve. The war will soon be felt here as it has been in the East."

" Just Indian raids, sir, and we've lived through quite a few of them."

The old man turned. " No, there's more to it than Indian raids. We've had them before and we'll have them again. Right now it's Texans bothering us. Texas Mounted Rifles! They already hold southern New Mexico and part of Arizona as well."

" Probably just a bluff, sir."

The fierce eyes seemed to lash out at Steve. " Bluff? You're talking just like the rest of the fools who cannot, and will not, believe those Texans mean business! Supposing those rebels do attack and conquer New Mexico? Do you know what they stand to gain? "

Steve shook his head. He still thought his uncle was building up a big case out of nothing.

" If the Texans conquer New Mexico and capture the vast military stores at Fort Union, they could arouse Southern sympathies all over the Southwest. They could gain many recruits, arm them, then strike west through Arizona to attack California. Once California was in their hands, the Union might suffer a blow that would lose the war for them."

" How so, sir? "

" California and the rest of the Pacific Coast have fine deepwater ports. The Pacific slopes are covered with fine timber for shipbuilding. There's the Mare Island Navy Yard and the Benecia Arsenal. Ships from all over the world could bring their goods to the Pacific Coast, sell them to the rebels, who in turn would freight them across California, Arizona, New Mexico, and Texas, thence into the Confederacy! Do you follow me? "

" Yes, but the Union navy can blockade the Pacific Coast as it is now blockading the Atlantic Coast and the Gulf of Mexico, sir."

Judge Ames snorted. " Maybe! But did it ever occur to you that the Federal government gets most of its gold from the California mines? What happens if the rebels get possession of the California gold mines and the silver mines of Nevada? "

Steve paled a little. " I never thought of that."

" You'd better! The whole country had better! You don't run wars without gold and silver, son. The Romans could have told you that. Another thing: all we've got to hold New Mexico, the key to the whole situation, is a handful of Regulars backed by local militia and volunteers, and a great part of those militia and volunteer units are composed of native New Mexicans. Now these men are brave enough, but they have an inherent fear of the *tejanos,* as they call the Texans, and there doesn't seem to be much we can do about it."

The old man walked to a roller map that hung on the wall over a side table. He pulled it down, then placed the lamp on the side table so that the yellow light illuminated the parchment, and Steve saw that it was a great map of the Southwest. The old man began to talk again and as he did so he traced the course of his talk with a spatulate finger, and some of his past words began to make greater sense to Steve.

" The whole territory south of Albuquerque is practically a ghost country now, Steve. Apaches are ripping through it from one end to the other. Ranches, *placitas,* and mines have been abandoned. The few troops we have down there can hardly hold the Texans back, much less patrol hundreds of square miles of deserts and mountains to hold the Apaches in check."

Carter Ames began to touch crosses marked on the map in red ink. " You see these crosses? They mark the sites of half a dozen forts, once manned by Regular troops, that have been shamefully abandoned! Forts Bliss, McLane, Breckinridge, Buchanan, Fillmore, and Stanton. All we have left in the pathway of the advancing rebels is Fort Craig, on the Rio Grande near the Valverde Fords. If Fort Craig falls and our troops are driven from the field, the rebel flag will be flying over Santa Fe within a week after that."

Steve walked to the map. He could clothe that paper

with buttes and mesas, springs and water holes, trails and roads. He knew them well enough.

"After our recent disaster at San Augustine Springs," said his uncle, "our Regular troops at Fort Stanton abandoned it and set fire to it, then retreated to Fort Craig. For all we know, the Texans may have occupied Fort Stanton too."

"What happened at San Augustine Springs, sir?"

"Cowardice and treason! Major Isaac Lynde surrendered the entire garrison of Fort Fillmore after a shameful retreat from the fort itself. Seven companies of the Seventh United States Infantry and three companies of the Mounted Rifles. He surrendered five hundred well-trained and well-armed soldiers of the Regular army to three hundred poorly armed Texans without firing a shot! It seems incredible, but it did happen. Luke Comfort is down there now investigating the incident."

Steve smiled at recollection of the scout. "I hope the Apaches don't get him."

Judge Ames snorted. "Apaches get Luke Comfort? He can travel through the middle of their country and never be seen while he can see them. That's why the Mexicans call him El Espectro."

"The Ghost. It suits him all right."

The judge sat down and looked into the dying fire. "We are forming many new units here to fight against the Texans or any other rebels who figure on attacking us, but I doubt the value of most of these units. The people here have depended on U. S. troops ever since the American Occupation in 1846.

"There are not enough Americans to fill up the units and give them Yankee strength, so to speak. Then too, in addition to the Texan threat there are thirty to forty thousand hostile Indians running loose in the Southwest.

"We have some good men working for the Union though. Ceran St. Vrain commands your regiment, the First New Mexico Volunteers, and Kit Carson is his second in command. Those two men are worth at least a battalion apiece."

The judge filled the chocolate cups. "There are Southern agents working throughout the territory to incite the Indians and the native New Mexicans against the Union. They tell wild stories of the terrible *tejanos* and of how they each carry two huge razoredged bowie knives, double-barreled shotguns, a brace of revolvers, and lassos with which to hang any prisoners they catch. It is said too that they ride half-wild mustangs who have been trained to bite and kick their enemies."

Steve whistled softly.

"Trouble is, Stevie, that most of those wild tales are heartily believed by the native New Mexicans, at least those who have no education, and there are a lot of them. Our eastern politicians have forgotten us. They are so concerned with the war in Virginia and Tennessee they have forgotten their back door is wide open and banging back and forth in the wind of invasion. The Southwest, and possibly the entire Union, is in terrible danger here. The odds are high against us."

"And I thought I was leaving the war behind in Virginia!"

The fierce eyes studied him. "We need all the help we can get, Steve. Your place is rightfully here in New Mexico with your father and myself, as well as with all your friends, and before this war is over you'll be playing a man's part in it like a good many other boys about your age, Steve."

Steve stood up and walked to the door. "If you'll excuse me, sir, I'll attend to my horse."

"Go ahead, Steve."

Steve hesitated at the door and then turned. "If those were not *ladrones* who killed Lieutenant Bruce, they must have been Southern agents. And, if they were, why would they use a disguise such as they did?"

The old man stood up and came closer to Steve. "Because it is entirely possible that those men may have been well known here in New Mexico Territory — men who do not want their identity known, at least at this time."

" But why? "

The gray eyes half closed. " Because they are waiting to see which way the ball bounces, Steve. Obviously they want the South to win and will do everything they can to further the Southern cause, but if the South does not win, then they can still play the part of loyal Union men."

" That's about as sneaky a way as they can do it, sir."

A big hand closed on Steve's shoulder. " They play both sides, son. I'd rather have an enemy face to face with me and know he was a man of honor and who believed in his own cause. But such men as we have just spoken about have no honor and care not a whit about it. They seek personal gain only."

" Why can't they be rooted out? "

The old man spoke in a low, tense voice. " Because some of them are in high places. Positions of trust. We don't know for sure who they are or what their game is. There is only one thing we can do. Be ever alert! " He placed his hand on the butt of his pistol.

Steve opened the door and walked out in the patio. He had come home to a boiling pot of intrigue and suspicion and he knew now that the war had come to New Mexico as well as to the rest of the United States. There was no place in his great country, and no person who would not be affected by it, directly or indirectly, one way or another.

The air was bright and fresh with no sign of rain in the clear morning sky. There was a winy freshness in the mountain wind, now warmed by the sun, and carrying with it the odors of thyme, sage, and mint. Bright pools of water dotted the flagged patio. The rolling of a drum came from Fort Marcy, which overlooked the city. The echo had hardly died away in the nearby hills when it seemed to be mocked by the soft tolling of a chapel bell.

Zouave whinnied softly from his stall, and Steve went to feed the great dun. Steve's mind was racing with all that his uncle had told him, and he realized now that there was great danger in New Mexico as well as in Virginia and Tennessee, and that his wish to see action in the war could just as easily be fulfilled in his home country as it could be in the East. Suddenly he felt older, as though he too would have to play the part of a man, and he determined to do the best he could. He was a soldier, and a soldier served where he was ordered to serve, and Steve's place was in New Mexico Territory.

CHAPTER 6

Santa Fe, New Mexico Territory, September, 1861

THE SUN was well up when Steve and his uncle left the house and walked toward the plaza. Country people urged their shaggy little burros along with cudgel blows as they hurried toward the market. Ragged peons in dirty, grayish trousers and shirts shuffled through the mud of the street. The old familiar odor of the city seemed to settle about Steve — piñon smoke, the strong odors of many horses and burros, the perfume of flowers threading through it all.

Two-wheeled *carretas* groaned past on shrieking, ungreased wheels, and the ringing of metal on metal came from a nearby blacksmith shop. Steve shook his head. "Santa Fe hasn't changed much," he said.

"Not outwardly, Steve, but underneath the peacefulness there is a lot of tension."

They entered the plaza and walked toward the low Governor's Palace. Rows of country people sat beneath the shade of the long roof that ran the length of the palace and shielded the sidewalk. Heaps of melons, shiny white onions, potatoes, apples, and squash lay on squares of dirty cloth. Long strings of scarlet chili pods hung from the great posts of silvery wood that supported the roof overhead. The canvas stalls stretched along the west side of the building. Pigs grunted, turkeys gobbled, and vendors shouted their wares along the line of stalls. Here and there were stolid Indians from the pueblos, muffled in cheap trade blankets, saying nothing but watching everything.

Steve and his uncle walked into the dimly lighted palace. A sergeant major of Regulars sat at a desk. " Good morning, Judge Ames," he said with a smile.

" I must see the colonel at once, Sims."

The sergeant major stood up. " Just a moment, sir." He walked into a hallway, and they could hear his voice mingled with that of another man. In a moment he was back. " The colonel is in conference. Captain DeWitt will see you though."

Carter Ames nodded shortly. " Come on, Steve," he said.

They walked down the hallway and entered a small room. An officer sat at a desk. He stood up as Carter Ames entered. "Good morning, Judge," he said cordially.

" Morning, Captain. This young man is my nephew, Steven Ames, just arrived from the East. Steve, this is Captain Milas DeWitt, one of Colonel Canby's aides."

DeWitt held out a hand to Steve and smiled as Steve saluted. " A real soldier? " he said with a faint tinge of satire in his cultured voice.

Carter Ames nodded. " Steve fought at Bull Run with the New York Volunteers."

The curiously light-blue eyes of the officer studied Steve. " I don't suppose you're too proud of that, Steve? "

Steve flushed. The man was trying to annoy him, and Steve had a feeling that his uncle didn't care too much for the officer either. "The Union troops fought well, sir," he said. "It was a battle that could have gone either way. In my opinion the rebels were luckier than we were."

"Perhaps. Perhaps." The officer looked at Carter Ames. " I'll take the dispatches, Judge."

" They are for Colonel Canby, sir."

"The colonel is very busy. When he is through with his

conference he must leave for Galisteo. Let me have the dispatches, and they'll be in his hands so that he can study them on his trip."

Judge Ames glanced at Steve. Steve raised his head. "The orders were that the dispatches were to be placed in Colonel Canby's hands, Captain."

A muscle in the officer's left cheek began to twitch a little. "Perhaps you didn't understand me, young man."

"He did, DeWitt," said the judge. "But he has his orders."

"From whom?"

"From Lieutenant Lloyd Bruce, sir," said Steve. "He told me to deliver these dispatches personally to Colonel Canby and to no other person."

"So?" The officer leaned forward. "And where is this officer, may I ask?"

"Dead in Glorieta Pass, DeWitt," said Carter Ames. "Ambushed and murdered by Jicarillas. The boy got the dispatches and broke through the Jicarillas to get here with the case."

DeWitt held out a hand. "I'm sorry to hear about Bruce. Good work, young Steven Ames. Now I must have those papers."

"No, sir," said Steve.

For a moment the room was very quiet. Then Captain DeWitt leaned forward. "Perhaps you don't understand," he said slowly and clearly. "I represent the colonel. The colonel is too busy to bother with such matters as these. Now give me that case!"

Carter Ames seemed to grow a little in height, and his eyes took on the fierce, frosty look Steve knew so well. "You seem to feel that these dispatches are rather trivial, sir," he said coldly. "Such is not the case. An officer died to get them here. My nephew fought his way through Jicarillas to get them here. They go into Colonel Canby's hands and into no one else's! Now maybe you understand!"

Captain DeWitt straightened up. " What right have you to interfere in military affairs, sir? "

Carter Ames waved a hand. " This is not a parade ground at West Point, Captain. This is New Mexico. We New Mexicans are all interested in military affairs, and as a member of the military committee of the territory, appointed by Governor Connelly himself, I see no reason why I should not take an interest in the defense of this territory."

" Well spoken, sir," a quiet voice said behind Steve. He turned quickly to look at a tall officer wearing silver eagles on his shoulder bars.

Carter Ames turned. " Here is Colonel Canby now, Steve. Give him the dispatches."

Steve saluted and handed the case to the officer. Canby smiled. " I expected an officer to deliver these, young man."

" Lieutenant Bruce was killed last night in Glorieta Pass by Jicarillas, sir. At least . . ." Steve's voice trailed off as he saw the look in his uncle's eyes.

" At least what? " questioned the colonel.

Steve swallowed. " Nothing, sir."

" My nephew was riding with the lieutenant as orderly, Colonel," said the judge quickly. " Bruce was killed, and Steven here got the dispatches and rode to Santa Fe with them."

The colonel studied Steve. " My personal thanks to you, Steven Ames. Come, Judge, let's look these over."

" Steve, wait outside for me," said Carter Ames.

" No," said Canby. " Let him come too. He risked his life for these dispatches. It's only right to assume he wouldn't reveal their contents."

Captain DeWitt started to come around his desk, but Canby stopped him with a wave of his left hand. "DeWitt, I want you to go to Galisteo for me."

There was an odd look in DeWitt's eyes when the three of them left the office.

Canby seated himself at his desk and fiddled with the dispatch case lock. " You have the key? " he asked Steve.

" No, sir. Lieutenant Bruce carried it in his boot. There was no time to get it."

" And why not? "

Steve allowed the ghost of a smile to drift across his face. "I was a little busy at the time, Colonel."

Canby nodded. He took a knife from a desk drawer and began to slit the thick leather of the case. " You are sure you were ambushed by Jicarillas? "

Steve looked at the judge. The judge nodded. " No, sir," said Steve.

Canby's head snapped up. " What do you mean, sir? "

Steve explained what had happened.

Canby leaned back in his chair and looked at Carter Ames. " What do you think, Judge? "

" How many people knew about those dispatches? "

" Here? "

" Yes."

Canby steepled his fingers. " Myself, you, Judge, your brother Mark, Governor Connelly, Captain Florian, and Captain DeWitt."

" No others? "

" Not to my knowledge."

Carter Ames rested an arm over the back of his chair. " There must have been a leak somewhere then."

"Yes."

" My brother Mark is down south and has been down there ever since he came back from Independence. You know I kept my mouth shut, and certainly the governor did. I know you didn't speak about the papers to anyone but those people you have named."

" That leaves Captains DeWitt and Florian," blurted out Steve.

Colonel Canby's eyes were a little cold when he looked at Steve. " Both trusted officers and gentlemen. Captain DeWitt has been traveling through the northern parts of the territory for the past few months on defense business."

" And Florian? " asked Carter Ames.

Canby flushed a little. " He has been here. The man is careless, and perhaps a bit of a fool, but he is no traitor, sir."

" Let us hope not, Colonel."

Canby took out the dispatches and began to scan them swiftly, and his expression changed from one of hope to one of disappointment. Finally he looked up. " I had hoped for better news. I had requested many stands of arms, Springfield or Enfield .58 caliber rifles. Instead, they say they will send me a shipment of large-calibered Austrian muskets and other junk picked up from foreign governments eager to sell their antique equipment to the gullible Americans so that they can rearm themselves with the latest weapons at our expense.

" The Government expects little action here in New Mexico and they intend to transfer my Regulars back east where they are more sorely needed!

" I had expected some information on when my troops will be paid, but there is nothing here mentioning pay at all. The Regulars have not been paid in nine months and the Volunteers have never been paid at all.

" They say I might get help in time, but for the time being I must hold this territory with the troops I have, less the Regulars."

Carter Ames smashed a fist down on the arm of his chair. " Great news! Supposing the Texans find that out? It is probably their fear of the Regulars that has made them move so slowly thus far. The Texans had poor arms until Major Lynde delivered the best we had to them by his surrender at San Augustine Springs. Supposing they find out we're getting foreign stuff with which to arm our men. Those Texans will not have to shoot us out of the territory. They'll laugh us out! "

Canby rubbed his jaws. " There is more news. There is information about a rebel column coming up through the

Panhandle of Texas to attack us, and perhaps another one up the Pecos."

"Great! Great!" snapped the judge.

Canby stood up and looked out of the window into the patio. "If all this information had gotten into the wrong hands, it would have speeded up the rebel invasion. I know you two gentlemen will keep it to yourselves. Perhaps I should have kept it to myself rather than to put fear into others."

"We're not whipped yet, Colonel."

"No . . . but things are getting worse. We're a long way from help here, Judge." The colonel turned. "How was the trip on the Santa Fe Trail, young Ames?"

"The Kiowas tried to cut off some of our men. Pawnees trailed us, trying to get at our horses and mules. Three hunters were killed near Salt Bottoms. There was hardly a time, sir, after we reached the Arkansas when we weren't being watched by hostile Indians."

Canby nodded. "I expect travel on the trail to be closed before too long. We cannot afford to spare enough troops as escorts. In time we'll be cut off completely from the East. It is then we'll have to fight with our backs against the wall." The colonel held out his hand to Steve. "Thank you in the name of the territorial government for your courage and loyalty in bringing these dispatches safely to me."

Steve shook the officer's hand and then stepped back and saluted.

"Wait for me outside, Steve," said his uncle.

Steve walked out of the office and through the hallway past DeWitt's office, but the officer wasn't at his desk. Steve stopped outside underneath the great roof and watched the busy market business.

"You mustn't think me hard to get along with, Steve," a voice said behind him.

Steve turned. It was Captain DeWitt, booted and spurred, with his saddlebags hanging over his arm. "You were doing your duty, sir," said Steve quietly. At least I think you were doing your duty, he thought.

" You must understand that an aide must act as a buffer, so to speak, between a superior officer and those who might annoy him with trivial matters."

Such as dispatches from Washington, thought Steve.

" I don't want you or your uncle to think I have anything personal against either one of you."

" We don't, sir."

" How did the Federal troops behave at Bull Run? "

" We fought well. We were green and they were green. They had better leadership I think."

" Still, I wonder if we can be sure of the final victory? "

Steve stared at him. " Have you any doubt, Captain? "

DeWitt laughed. " Certainly not! But we must take Bull Run as the measure of things until other battles are fought."

" My regiment fought well enough. We made mistakes. When Stuart's cavalry charged we tried to reload after firing a volley when we should have met them with the bayonet. Experienced troops wouldn't have done that. We were smashed. We made mistakes at Bull Run and so did they, but we made the biggest mistakes. The biggest one of all was in thinking we had the battle won before it had really been settled. It won't happen again."

" On to Richmond," said DeWitt dryly.

" One battle doesn't decide a war, sir."

" No, it doesn't, but here in New Mexico we have rancher majors and storekeeper colonels. The policy here seems to be to promote a man for *whom* he knows rather than for *what* he knows."

" There are not enough trained men to meet the emergency, Captain. That's what my colonel said."

DeWitt nodded. He looked across the plaza and seemed to talk almost to himself. " There will be great opportunities here for the right man. Opportunities to be snatched and developed when the time comes, and to the devil with the hindmost."

Steve looked at him surreptitiously. There was a faraway look on the handsome face of the aide.

An orderly brought up a fine gray horse and saluted DeWitt. DeWitt turned and smiled at Steve as the orderly placed the saddlebags on the horse. " Perhaps we shall serve together yet, young Ames. I may need a good orderly when the time for fighting comes. If you do your duty as you did last night, I can't think of a better choice for an orderly."

" Thank you, sir."

DeWitt mounted, returned Steve's snappy salute, and then kneed his gray through the crowds in the plaza, followed by his orderly.

" That'll be the day," said Steve aloud.

Carter Ames stopped beside Steve. " A strange man," he said as they walked back toward their house.

" How so, sir? "

The judge looked around at the straight back of the aide. " West Point graduate. Left the service a year or so before the war and went to Texas and Mexico. Some say he was in business down there. Others say he was a spy for the abolitionist movement. No one really knows. But he came back into Federal Service when Fort Sumter was fired upon and was offered the position of aide by Colonel Canby because Canby knew DeWitt was acquainted with this country and the people. He's been of invaluable help to the colonel. They say he's slated for a high command when the fighting starts. I have no doubt but what he'll do well at that too. He's an expert shot with rifle and pistol, and they say he fences like a musketeer and rides like a Cossack."

" High praise, sir. It isn't like you to give one man so much praise."

Carter Ames tugged at his beard. " No, Stevie," he admitted. " There's one thing I know for sure about Captain Milas DeWitt."

" And that is? "

" I don't like him! "

They walked on to the house and once they were inside the judge looked at Steve and took him by the arm. " The colonel is well pleased with you. I suggested you be kept here in Santa Fe as messenger, orderly, and so forth, for the time being at least."

Steve flushed. " I'd rather be with my regiment."

" You can do better work for the Union here."

" How so? "

Carter Ames looked behind him as though someone might be eavesdropping. " You speak Spanish like a native, Steve. You know and like these people, and they know and like you. A smart lad like yourself can keep out of sight and keep his eyes and ears open and his mouth shut. Do you follow me? "

" Yes, sir! "

The judge winked. " I knew you would! "

" What do I do first, sir? "

" Get out of that uniform. Few of these people know you've been in uniform. None of them know you're in the First New Mexico. Get into civilian clothing and get out and see your friends in Santa Fe. Learn all you can."

" Is that all, sir? "

" It's a beginning, Steve. The colonel was quite impressed by you." The judge walked into the house.

Steve shook his head. He had wanted to let his friends see him in uniform. He heard Zouave whinny and he went in to see the big dun. The words of the colonel swirled through his mind. " In time we'll be cut off completely from the East. It is then we'll have to fight with our backs against the wall."

CHAPTER 7

Santa Fe, New Mexico Territory,
October, 1861

THE RUMOR of the missing Government wagons had developed into a story of fact, and little else was being spoken about in Santa Fe. Twelve heavily laden wagons had left Fort Union, near Wagon Mound, bound for Fort Marcy at Santa Fe via Las Vegas and Glorieta Pass. They had passed through Las Vegas and somewhere in the vicinity of Starvation Peak they had vanished.

Steven Ames stood in the plaza near La Fonda, the great inn of Santa Fe, and listened to a trooper who was telling some of the people what had happened.

"It was a strange thing," the trooper said. "The wagons were in good shape, most of them almost new, and the teams were good ones. I was part of the escort under Sergeant Mason, ten troopers in all. Near Starvation Peak we saw some Jicarillas lurking about in the brush up ahead of us, so Sergeant Hampton takes six of us after them, leaving three troopers behind with the wagons. The teamsters were armed, so there wasn't too much to worry about. The Jicarillas took off like jack rabbits, and we were about to return to the wagons when we saw an army officer standing on a low ridge near the road. He yelled at us and waved his arms, and then the Jicarillas dragged him from sight.

" Sergeant Hampton led us in a charge up that ridge, and when we got to the top we saw the officer being dragged down a canyon. Hampton leads us on, and suddenly we got a volley from ambush, full in the face, and Hampton goes down dead along with another man.

" By the time we got into cover, the Jicarillas was gone. We waited half an hour, and then Corporal Grady scouts ahead. No trace of the Jicarillas at all, but we did find part of the officer's uniform. By then it was getting dusk, so we took the bodies back toward the wagons. We went slow because of the bodies and we weren't too anxious to run into another ambush.

" Well, we reached the place where the wagons had been. Wasn't hide nor hair of them there, friends. Nothing but a little manure on the road. No tracks. No horses. No wagons. No men. Nothing."

A man whistled softly.

The trooper wiped the sweat from his sunburned face. " I tell you it gave us an eerie feeling to be standing there in that empty road with two dead men lying across their saddles, and not a trace of twelve Government wagons and their teams."

" What was in the wagons? " asked a clerk from Houghton's general store.

" New Government rifles, powder, ball cartridges, caps, bullet molds, lead, medicinal stores, saddles, harness sets, sabers, and some cases of artillery shells. There was a pair of brass mountain howitzers too, dismounted, but it doesn't take long to put them together. Besides all that, there was sacked flour, beans, and a lot of other food supplies."

" Some haul," said the clerk.

" Jicarillas, you think? " asked a bearded militiaman.

The trooper shrugged and thrust out his hands, palms upward. " *¿Quién sabe?* Who knows? All I know is that the wagons vanished." The trooper turned and walked toward the street that led to Fort Marcy.

Steve shoved back his wide-brimmed hat. The troops

were in short enough supply as it was. The loss of those wagons was a hard blow to the territory.

"*¡Amigo mío!*" a voice cried, and Steve was hit with full force between the shoulder blades. He staggered and turned around to look into the smiling face of Hernán Calvillo, a boy with whom he had gone to school in Santa Fe and with whom he had been expelled more than once.

"*¡Querido amigo!*" yelled Steve. He hurled himself at Hernán and gripped him about his slim waist, lifting him up and dumping him hard on the dusty ground.

"Son of a goat!" cried Hernán as he pounded Steve on the back with both fists.

"*¡Hombrecito!*" coughed Steve as he scrambled on top of his friend.

"Here! Here!" a man cried out. "No fighting here, boys!"

They looked up through the wreathing dust in surprise. "Fighting?" asked Steve. "I was just greeting Hernán here. I haven't seen my *amigo* in two years."

Hernán was laughing so hard there were tears in his eyes.

The man shoved back his wide-awake hat and scratched his bald head. "Well, I'll be switched," he said. "Friends? I'd hate to see you two together if you were enemies."

Steve got up and pulled Hernán to his feet. Hernán gave him the *abrazo,* wrapping his arms about Steve's shoulders and thumping his back. "How you have grown!" he said. "Perhaps it was the salt air in Nueva York?"

"No," said Steve with a grin. "I was right puny there, but when I crossed into New Mexico on the way back I grew four inches and put on twenty pounds!"

The New Mexican's eyes were wide. "Is this true? Come, we leave at once. I, too, would grow four inches and put on twenty pounds."

They walked toward the Governors' Palace, and the dark eyes of the smaller boy hardly left Steve's face. "You did not forget Hernán then?"

"I have to admit I never got expelled once from Mr.

Albright's Academy for Boys and Young Gentlemen."

"Is that why you joined the army?"

They laughed again. Steve held the arm of his best friend. "Where have you been?" he asked. "No one seemed to know."

The gay face saddened a little. "My father and mother died with the smallpox. For a time I lived in Taos with Tío Gaspar, but he was a hard man to get on with. Then I lived in Galisteo with Tía Theresa, but she has seven children and there was little to eat. So then I went to live with Tía Rosa who used to keep house for you, and there I am learning the trade of a muleteer from Tío Eusebio Campos. He is a good man. Far too easy on me, Tía Rosa says."

"I am sorry to hear about your father and mother."

"*Gracias, amigo*. But they are with God now. Happier perhaps than they were here, for life was always hard for them."

"Can you stay with me for a time?"

Hernán shrugged. "Why not? My aunt and uncle have gone to a wedding in Las Vegas and they left me here on the way. They say I get into too much trouble."

"So?"

Hernán grinned. "I do not like weddings anyway." He threw back his shoulders. "So I will stay with my *compañero!*"

"What do you think about those missing wagons, Hernán?"

"A strange thing! How is it possible to make twelve big wagons vanish into thin air? Perhaps it was the work of evil spirits." Hernán swiftly crossed himself.

The sergeant major came across the plaza, carrying a uniform over his left arm. He beckoned to Steve. Steve and Hernán hurried to him. The sergeant major held up a blouse and a forage cap that had crossed brass saber insignia on it with the numeral three above them. "This look familiar, Ames?" he asked.

Steve examined the items. There was a crooked seam on the elbow of the left sleeve that he remembered sewing himself. " Yes, sergeant major," he said quietly. " This was Lieutenant Bruce's blouse. I sewed up that seam one night by firelight near the Cimarrón Crossing."

The sergeant major nodded. " We never did find his body, you know. This cap and blouse were found by Corporal Grady and his men when they were ambushed."

" They were supposed to have seen an officer," said Steve.

The noncom nodded. " Yes, wearing these items. It couldn't have been Lieutenant Bruce. Who could it have been? "

The three of them looked at one another, then the sergeant major turned away. " I'll tell Captain DeWitt what you told me," he said.

" Do," said Steve politely.

The noncom looked sharply at him, then walked away.

Hernán looked to the east. " It would be interesting to go there and see if we could find those wagons," he said. " I have a horse. He is small and sad, but he travels surprisingly well."

Steve grinned. " You know something, *amigo?* "

" What is it? "

" I too have a horse! "

" Then let's go! This place palls on me, *amigo!* "

They hurried toward the Ames house. It would be more than a thirty-mile ride, and they would have to camp out overnight, but both of them were well accustomed to sleeping under the stars.

Both horses stood in the patio, saddled and with cantle and pommel packs. Hernán had been right about his horse, whom he called by the noble name of El Diablo. Steve had buckled on his pistol belt and had placed his Sharps carbine in its saddle scabbard while he had rounded up a short-barreled Wells-Fargo Colt for Hernán and a muzzle-loading Enfield carbine, which had once belonged to his Aunt Rosa's first husband, Adolfo, the gardener.

"What will your uncle say?" asked Hernán as he tightened the girth on El Diablo.

"Nothing."

Hernán looked surprised. "Now that is news! Why, *amigo?*"

Steve grinned. "He's not here, that's why. He left for Taos yesterday on territorial business."

"And your father?"

"I haven't seen him since I left for New York two years ago. He's down south somewhere."

"On territorial business."

Steve looked at him quickly. "How do you know?"

Hernán shrugged. "Who doesn't know? He is a well-known man. Owner of a freighting business. Once an officer in the Army of Occupation that came here many years ago. A good friend of the governor and of the military commander. What else would he be doing?"

"You know a lot, *chico.*"

Hernán smiled crookedly. "I know too much. There is very little that goes on in this territory that is not known to Hernán Calvillo, the all-seeing one."

El Diablo turned his head and dropped his ears, raising a right hind foot. Hernán jumped away. "Oh, no, you don't, *caballo mío!*" he cried out.

Steve eyed the disreputable horse. "He sure knows you," he said dryly.

Hernán nodded. "He has heart this one. A real bravo. A drinker of the wind."

"You'd never know by looking at him, *amigo.*"

"Do not let appearances deceive you." Hernán sidled close to his sad-looking steed and patted him on the neck. "See? The fire in him?"

El Diablo stood hipshot with his eyes half closed, as though asleep on his feet, but Steve could see one evil eye studying him and he wisely kept away from the rear end of El Diablo.

" That is a fine *caballo* you have, Steve," said Hernán.

Steve nodded as he slapped Zouave on the rump. " My father bought him in Independence for me and left him there until I picked him up."

" Your father is the wise one with the *caballos,"* said Hernán. " See, he is a coyote dun. One of the race that dies before tiring. He will always be in the lead, *amigo."*

" Brío escondido," said Steve. It was a phrase well known to both of the boys. *Brío escondido,* " the hidden vigor." The dun had never tired on the long trip from Independence, and on that terrible night when Lieutenant Bruce had died and Steve had saved the dispatches, Zouave had been like a part of Steve as he had ridden down the Jicarillas and fled at a steady mile-eating pace through the pass to the slopes above Santa Fe.

Hernán led his mount toward the door and then he turned. " But you must report that you are leaving." he said to Steve.

" Report to whom? "

" To the army, *amigo."*

" I left the army in Washington, *hombrecito."*

" So? Are you not a drummer assigned to the First New Mexico Volunteers? "

Steve eyed his friend. " How did you know that? "

" *¡Ea pues!* " Hernán snapped his fingers.

" Go on," demanded Steve.

The ingratiating smile flowed over Hernán's face like the shadow of a swift cloud on the slopes of the Sangre de Cristos. " I said I was all-seeing, Steve."

Steve nodded sourly. He might have known. Word got around Hernán's people with the speed of light.

" So you will report, *amigo?* "

Steve wet his lips. There had been little for him to do in Santa Fe in the days he had been there. His uncle had said Canby had been pleased with him and that he was to be kept in Santa Fe, rather than to serve with his regiment, as messenger, orderly, and so forth. Steve had done little but walk around town and see his old friends and learn the latest news, all of which was already well known to Colonel Canby and to the meanest hostler at La Fonda inn.

"Steve?"

Steve shook his head. "Lead your horse down the side lanes," he said. "I'll meet you on the pass road out of sight of town."

"*¡Bueno!*" Hernán opened the outer gate and led El Diablo through it. In a little while Steve heard the clopping of hoofs on the side lane west of the great house.

Steve looked about the quiet patio. Both his father and his uncle were gone on territorial business, so they couldn't stop him. Colonel Canby was too busy to bother about the activities of a humble drummer boy in the First New Mexico. Steve had been given to believe that his immediate superior was Captain Milas DeWitt, but in the time Steve had been in Santa Fe the captain had not bothered with him nor he with the captain. It was simple enough. He would go with Hernán. They'd certainly never miss the two of them in Santa Fe, and perhaps he and Hernán could find out something about those mysteriously vanished wagons.

He led Zouave to the gate and opened it, leading the dun out into the sunlit street. He ground-reined the horse, then walked back into the house, closing the great door and barring it so that he could leave by the smaller door and lock it behind him. As he reached for the door latch of the smaller door he suddenly remembered something. The silver trumpet! He had carried it from Washington with him and had placed it within the wardrobe in his room.

He stood there for a while, wondering if he should take the trumpet with him or not, then decided against it. The going might be rough, and he wanted no harm to come to it. He went to his room and got the instrument. For a moment he uncovered it and eyed it, remembering where and how he had come by it. It seemed so long ago, and yet the voice of Dacey Curtis seemed to pass through Steve's mind, handing the trumpet on to him. Big chance there was for

Steven Ames to use the trumpet to help either Yankee or rebel, or both. New Mexico was too far away from a smoky battlefield in Virginia and the bequest of a romantically minded boy who was dying even as he spoke.

Steve covered the trumpet and carried it into the living room. There were many *ladrones* in Santa Fe, but they knew better than to steal anything that might be too easily identified. Gold and silver were what they wanted. Still, the trumpet had silver in it; its very tone let anyone know that. Steve opened his mother's piano and placed the trumpet inside it. He softly closed the rosewood lid, looked around the big room once, then left it.

He led Zouave down a side lane and through narrow, winding streets until he was south of the town, near the road to Albuquerque; then he cut across country to pick up the road leading southeast to Glorieta Pass.

The wind was fresh and dry as he rode, and in the distance cloud shadows chased themselves along the purple mountain slopes. He eyed the rough country to the east. Somewhere within those jumbled mountains was the secret of the lost wagons. Slowly he forgot about Bull Run, Dacey Curtis, the silver trumpet, Santa Fe, Captain DeWitt, and everything else except the fact that he had a fine horse beneath him, an open road, a good companion, and an adventurous quest.

Chapter 8

Sangre de Cristo Mountains,
October, 1861

STEVE AMES opened his eyes and looked up at the dim roof of the cave. It was cold in the predawn darkness, but he was snug enough under his thick trade blanket. He raised his head and saw the shadowy outline of Hernán's steeple hat against the outer light. A cold wind was keening up the pass below the cave.

They had ridden swiftly from the time they had met on the road until just after dusk, when they had stopped to make their camp. The horses were picketed in a shallow box canyon a quarter of a mile from the cave. It was a procedure both of them had learned in Indian country, for a snorting or whinnying horse would give away a camp.

What troubled Steve was the fact that the road from Las Vegas, which trended almost due south then turned northwesterly through the Sangre de Cristos by way of Glorieta Pass and Apache Canyon, had been safe enough from the predatory Jicarillas for some time before the war. There was always plenty of traffic on that road. Santa Fe Trail caravans, stagecoaches, parties of well-armed traders, and troops of cavalry had made it a bad place for raiding Indians. It was true that the war had given Indians a rather free rein in New Mexico, but even so, it had sent more and more troops traveling both ways through the passes.

Yet Lieutenant Bruce had been killed eighteen miles from Santa Fe, presumably by Jicarillas, and the twelve wagons from Fort Union had vanished like melting snow on the lower slopes of the Sangre de Cristos on a warm day, and no one had any idea what had happened to them.

Hernán moved a little. He was swathed in a thick serape, and his carbine barrel thrust itself up from beneath the serape like a stalk of ocotillo. He looked like some strange thorny growth of the desert as he sat there, watching the canyon below the cave.

" Hernán," said Steve.

" *¿Sí?* "

" See anything? "

" Nothing but ghosts, *amigo.* This is a haunted place, Stevie."

Steve sat up. " Let's eat and get out of here."

Hernán arose and stretched himself. " I do not like this place. As I said, it is haunted."

Steve snorted. " By what? "

Hernán shrugged. " Many things. You know the Pecos Ruins. They say there were once over two thousand Pueblo Indians living there. The Conquistadores treated them harshly. Apaches and Comanches raided them. Smallpox and mountain fever did the rest. In 1540, according to the padres, they had two thousand people. Now, in 1861, there is no one left there."

The dark eyes studied Steve. " You do not believe some of their spirits are still in this place? "

" *¿Quién sabe?* "

"Many travelers have been killed by Jicarillas and *ladrones* in here. You can see the crosses over their graves almost every mile. Do *they* not haunt this place? "

Steve placed dried meat and cold beans on their tin plates and uncorked his big felt-covered canteen. " I'm interested only in a particular type of ghost, *amigo mío.*"

" Yes? "

Steve looked up. "The ghosts of twelve wagons loaded with military supplies."

There was a long silence and then Hernán spoke again. "And the ghost of Lieutenant Bruce?"

Steve nodded.

"You do not believe those were Jicarillas who killed him?"

"No."

"White men?"

"Yes."

Hernán gnawed at the dried beef. "I know of the Jicarillas. They used to live far north of here, but the Comanches drove them south. For a time they adopted the Christian faith and accepted Spanish rule, then they joined their cousins the Mescaleroes and raided both Pueblo and Spaniard alike. But they have not been active in this pass for a long time, Steve."

"No."

Hernán digested his thought as he had the beef. "Then what are we looking for, *amigo?*"

Steve stood up. "Not ghosts, *amigo,* that is for certain."

They gathered their gear together and left the cave to go to the horses. The false dawn was graying the eastern sky, and they could see the seven-thousand-foot bulk of Starvation Peak dimly against the coming light. It was said that over a hundred colonists had taken refuge up there when pursued by Indians long ago and had starved to death. More ghosts, thought Steve.

"This must be the place," said Hernán as he stopped leading El Diablo and looked up at Steve.

Steve nodded. There was a ridge to their left a short distance from the wagon road, the only true ridge for miles.

They led the horses transversely up the ridge.

"Look here," said Hernán. He placed a finger on what looked like splashes of quicksilver on the rocks. He has eyes like an eagle, thought Steve. They were bullet splashes and quite fresh too. There was something else on a flat rock ledge, a dark stain, and both of them knew what that was. Men had died right there.

Steve squatted on the ridge top and looked down at the road while Hernán scurried through the brush like a hunting beagle.

The canyon was well lighted, and the road wound along like a tattered ribbon. There was no sign of life except for a hawk hung like a scrap of charred paper high in the updraft over the canyon.

Steve scanned both sides of the road with his uncle's field glasses. The old man would have been angry at him for taking the glasses, although he hadn't used them himself for years. They were good German glasses, made by Vollmer of Jena, and Carter Ames thought a lot of them. So did Steve.

Hernán pattered back down the slope. "Look," he said. He held out his hand. He held the string-tied tops of paper cartridges, the type of cartridge that is contained with powder and ball in stiff paper. The top of the cartridge is bitten off by the shooter, then the powder is dumped into the rifle barrel, followed by the ball, and finally the paper as a wad to hold them in place.

Such cartridges were common enough, but it probably marked the place where the Jicarillas had been firing on the troopers.

"See anything?" asked Hernán as he dropped the papers.

"I'm not sure." Steve handed the glasses to Hernán. "Look across the road at that little grove of trees. There's a dry wash behind it."

Hernán took the glasses and studied the place. He whistled softly. "Let's take a closer look, Stevie."

They led the horses down the ridge and across the road, tethering them among the trees. Every now and then both boys scanned the heights and at such times they tightened their hands on their gunstocks. It was quiet in the canyon, almost too quiet.

Steve went down on one knee and studied the tracks in the bottom of the dry wash. There had been no rain in that country since the night he had ridden into Santa Fe. Here, on the hard gravelly bottom of the wash, could be seen faint hoof and wheel tracks, a good hundred yards from the wagon road. Steve looked down the road both ways and saw no place where big army wagons could have been hidden, nor did it look as though wagons could have been hauled over the ridge to the north of the road.

Steve stood up and looked up the wash. It seemed to vanish into the heights south of the road.

"Who would take wagons in there, Steve?" asked Hernán thoughtfully.

Without another word they went back to get their horses, then led them slowly up the wash, between brush-lined banks, until they could no longer see the road behind them but only the brush and to the south of them the rugged heights of the canyon wall.

The wash banks became higher and higher until at last the boys were walking in a narrow gorge, and it didn't seem as though anyone would take a wagon through there, but now and then they saw where metal-tired wheels had scoured into the harsh gravelly earth, and there were horse and mule droppings all along the way.

But still the gorge wall got higher and higher until they were walking in a semidimness, cut off from the early morning sun, and a cold wind blew against their faces as they kept on.

Hernán wet his lips. "Perhaps these are not the wagons?" he suggested vaguely.

"Who else would haul wagons in here?"

Hernán shrugged. "Who else?" he echoed.

They had covered several miles it seemed, and they expected the narrow slot in which they walked to close in at a dead end, but suddenly it widened. They had been climbing steadily, and Hernán looked up fearfully at pieces of whitened driftwood that had caught in crevices and on ledges high above them. The place would be a death trap in a flash storm. " How did the sky look to you, *amigo?* " he asked quietly.

Steve glanced at him. " Bright. Why? "

" You saw no clouds? "

" None."

" You are sure? "

Steve scratched his chin. " Come to think of it, I saw some heavy clouds forming over Starvation Peak just before we came in here."

" *¡Dios en cielo!* "

Steve grinned as he walked on.

The gorge widened, and although they covered long stretches in which they saw no signs of wheels or tracks, there was always something that led them on — a broken branch of brush, an uprooted rock. Both boys knew that a rock settles with its heavy side down and that in time the part beneath the surface becomes darker; therefore a rock with its heavy and dark side up had been displaced.

They came out into a wider canyon, and beyond it they could see a notch against the sky. The canyon was as lonely as the grave, and the simile made Steve feel a little nervous.

Hernán shoved back his heavy steeple hat and wiped his face. " If we keep on this way, Steve, I'll be back in Galisteo before dusk."

Steve nodded. He was a little puzzled. He was sure they were following the tracks of the missing wagons, but why were they headed this way? If the Jicarillas had stolen them, they would have looted their haul, taking what pleased their odd fancies and ruining or burning the rest. The wagons would have been abandoned or burned, and the horses and mules taken for transportation or food. No Indian likes to use a wagon, and in certainty, there was little enough area in their hidden haunts where a wagon could be used.

" Shall we go on? " asked Hernán.

" Why not? "

" Why not, indeed? We can come out on the Galisteo road and ride north to Santa Fe. A nice, roundabout ride, in which we learn nothing, my little goat."

" Don't be too sure, *hombrecito.*"

The sun was high now, and the heat of it flooded the canyon as they crossed toward the far side; in a place where water had flowed across soft flats they found deep, rutted tracks where the wagons had been pulled across.

" It must be *ladrones,*" said Hernán thoughtfully. " No Indian would take such pains to get these wagons through here."

"Si." said Steve quietly. "But no *ladróne* would be caught with a Government wagon and Government mules and horses. The troopers shoot first and ask questions later. You know that as well as I do."

They rested in the early afternoon, picketing the horses in a hollow. Steve lay back with his hat tilted across his face. According to Hernán, they would come out into the Galisteo Valley area, which was about twenty miles due south of Santa Fe. Roads led south and southwest from the area, through the mountains, and there were many little communities throughout. Scarcely the place for anyone attempting to smuggle stolen Government goods through without being seen, for the people were noted for their curiosity about travelers.

There were quite a few pueblo ruins in the Galisteo Valley, nine of them in fact, two on the north side and seven on the south side in the Galisteo Basin. No Indians had lived in them for over half a century, and the simple farming people of Galisteo left them strictly alone because of their superstitions concerning the brooding relics.

Hernán came prowling through the brush and scrub trees. " It is as I thought," he said quietly. " The wagons have passed through the notch, but where have they gone from there? "

" All we can do is follow the tracks."

Hernán squatted beside Steve. " Supposing we catch up with the thieves? "

Steve shoved back his hat and sat up. " Why . . ." His voice trailed off.

" *Sí,*" said Hernán wisely. " We left Santa Fe to find the wagons, although we did not expect to find them. But we found the tracks. The wagons could not have flown from here. Therefore they went through the notch. How much farther can they have gone? "

Steve stood up and reached for his carbine.

" Eh, *amigo?* " asked Hernán.

Steve looked at him. " Do you want to go back? "

Hernán looked at the jumble of mountains through which they had come, and the memories of that narrow gorge with its shadows and brooding thoughts was a little too much for him. " No," he said quietly.

" Then we go on! *¡Vámonos!* "

They led the horses toward the notch.

Hernán wet his lips, then shifted his carbine from one hand to the other, constantly drying the free hand from sweat. Not until they had cleared the notch did he seem to get confidence back into himself. " Eh," he laughed. " I was afraid of an ambush back there, *amigo!* How foolish can one — " His voice stopped short as the sound of a breaking stick came to them. A bush high on the slopes to the left of them seemed to blossom in white and red, and Hernán's steeple hat was removed from his head as though by an invisible hand. The echo of the shot slammed back and forth in the notch and then died away.

The two boys slapped their horses on the rumps, and dived for cover in a brushy wash. They eyed the quiet slopes.

" Jicarillas? " said Hernán at last in a curiously dry voice.

" No Indian can shoot like that, *amigo!* That was almost two hundred yards from here."

" *Sí.*"

They scanned the slopes. Steve uncased his uncle's

glasses and studied the area. There was no sign of life.

" Let's go," said Steve.

" Where? "

" To the Galisteo Valley of course! "

Hernán smiled faintly. " Perhaps we should go back the other way? "

" We'd have to pass through the last part of it after dark."

" *Sí.*"

They crawled along to where the horses had stopped beside a rugged upthrust of rock, and led them down the slope. Steve looked to the left as they passed the place where the hidden marksman had been. There was an opening into the heights. It was then he saw the movement of the brush and he threw a shoulder against Hernán, driving him to the ground as the marksman fired again, and this time El Diablo was struck on the flank. He reared and snorted, and took off at a dead run down the valley, with a worm of blood trickling down his dusty flank.

The boys lay flat on the stony ground. Steve cocked his Sharps and checked the range up to the place where the thin smoke drifted amidst the brush. Two hundred yards at least, a long shot, and nothing to sight upon.

Hernán crossed himself.

Steve wet his lips. They were in good cover. Zouave was in a hollow. " Stay here," he said quietly to his companion.

He inched his way along the slope until he was a good fifty yards from Hernán, then cautiously raised his head. There was something alien on the slope, a darker patch of shadow, and the brush moved a little, although there was no wind.

Steve flipped up his back sight and set it at two hundred yards. He rested the heavy barrel on a rock and sighted on the place where he saw the brush moving.

Something protruded through the bush like a snake, and the sun glinted on a rifle barrel. The barrel was pointed down toward where Hernán lay hidden.

Steve cuddled down against the stock of his carbine. He

picked up the knife-blade front sight of the carbine with his eyes, and settled it squarely into the notch of the rear sight. He moved the carbine a little until he was sighting approximately where a man would be lying if he was holding that rifle through the brush.

Hernán moved quickly. The rifle spouted flame and smoke, and at that instant Steve pressed trigger. The Sharps kicked back hard against his shoulder, and for a moment his sight was obscured by the smoke of the discharge. Then he saw a movement in the brush. A man had stood up, dropping his rifle. Gripping his right wrist, he buckjumped through the brush to vanish into a jumble of rocks and scrub trees.

"Good shooting, *amigo!*" called out Hernán cheerfully.

Steve reloaded. "Yeah," he said dryly. "Thanks for setting him up, but as good as he is, he might have put a slug through your thick head!"

Steve crawled to Hernán and they lay there a long time looking up the slope, but there was no sign of life. The rifle lay in the sun below the brush where the marksman had been hidden when he had fired.

Steve placed his carbine beside Hernán. "Keep me covered," he said.

"Where are you going?"

"To get that rifle."

"But we have good guns, *amigo!*"

Steve nodded. "But not that one." He slid into a gully and trotted along it until he reached a thick brushy patch. As he angled up the slope, with his cocked pistol in his hand, there was no sound or sign of life. The valley below him was as peaceful looking as one could imagine.

He crawled toward the rifle and got it, looking about on the ground as he did so. Bright flecks of blood were on the rocks. He peered up the slope toward that mysterious opening but thought better of trying to see where it went.

Steve went back to join Hernán, and they examined the rifle. It was new. A .58 caliber Springfield with the Government stamp upon it.

" What does it prove? " asked Hernán.

Steve tapped the stamped serial number on the rifle. " Someone has a record of the rifles carried in those wagons. Maybe this is one of them."

" So? "

Steve pointed toward the dim opening in the heights to the south. " Where would that go? "

" Into the Galisteo Basin, not far from the southern ruins."

" What's in there besides ruins? "

" Nothing much. A deserted mission. A few abandoned houses." Hernán wet his lips. " You're not thinking of going up there, are you?

" We'd be fools to try. Someone wanted to keep us from going up there. He did a good job. We'd better get out of here. I have a feeling it wouldn't be too healthy in here after dark."

Hernán breathed a sigh of relief. " You know, *amigo,*" he said quietly, " I have exactly the same idea."

They walked toward the far mouth of the valley with Steve leading Zouave. A horse whinnied in the distance and El Diablo appeared, galloping loosely. He stopped near Hernán and whinnied softly. Hernán examined the wound. " It is only of the flesh," he said with a smile. " I will see to it in Galisteo." He patted the ungainly horse. " You see how he loves me? "

Steve nodded.

Hernán turned to pick up his carbine and as he did so El Diablo's ears went back and before Steve could yell a warning the horse had neatly planted both hind hoofs against the seat of Hernán's baggy pants, driving him swiftly into a thicket of catclaw.

Steve pulled Hernán from the thicket. The boy shook his fist at the horse. Tears of rage and pain were in his eyes. Steve couldn't help laughing. " See how he loves you, *amigo?* " he said.

Hernán picked up his carbine, rubbed the seat of his

pants, and set off down the valley, the very picture of outraged dignity.

Steve thrust the rifle he had found through the straps of his cantle pack. Taking the bridle reins of both horses, he followed Hernán. Now and then he looked back toward the place where he had wounded the mysterious rifleman. Something was up there — something that was well guarded. Even now sharp eyes might be watching them.

It would be best to stay in Galisteo that night. Then, in the morning, they could go into the basin and scout about, acting the part of hunters, for Steve fully believed that those missing wagons were somewhere within a few miles of him.

CHAPTER

9

Galisteo, New Mexico Territory,
October, 1861

GALISTEO was sleeping in the late afternoon sun. Green clouds of cottonwoods seemed to rest against the dun hills. The dying sun turned the thick-walled adobe houses into golden cubes, accented by the blue-painted doors and the scarlet strings of chilies that hung from the projecting roof beams. A wraith of smoke hung low over the little village, mingling with the late afternoon haze.

" Is it not pretty? " asked Hernán of Steve.

New Mexico was a dream in September and October. The war seemed so far away, and yet the bullet hole in Hernán's hat seemed more real than the beautiful Galisteo Basin.

The air was crisp and winy, and now and then the quiet was broken by the high, clear bugle notes of prairie larks. The beautiful birds fluttered about the water tanks and the bright flowing irrigation ditches. The larks, with their white-bordered tails and their golden breasts with jet-black necklaces, caught the eyes of the boys as they rode along.

" Even the mockingbird cannot imitate the prairie lark," said Hernán. " Listen! "

The bugle call seemed to ring in the quiet air.

" The lark has no death in its soul, my mother used to say," said Hernán softly.

As they reached the outskirts of the town they could see the little *pajaritos,* " swallows," thick around the houses.

Steve wrinkled his nose. The sandy streets were littered with offal amidst which pigs, dogs, and chickens rooted for scraps while half-naked children added to the swarm. The odor of piñon smoke mingled with the stench of the rotting waste in the streets.

They rode toward the little plaza. Hernán turned in his saddle. " They have organized a militia company here. Many men have joined it. But the weapons are all junk. They could have used some of those fine rifles which were in the missing wagons." The boy waved a hand. " These are simple people and they do not like war, but they are willing to fight for New Mexico."

How well will they fight? thought Steve. He didn't want to hurt his friend's feelings, but he knew how little value was placed on these peon soldiers by the territorial officials. They knew little about weapons and shooting as compared to the tough Texas rebels who had been raised in the saddle and teethed on pistols and rifles.

" Look," said Hernán, " there are two officers! One of them is Capitán Padilla of the militia. I do not know the other one."

" I do," said Steve quietly. It was Captain Milas DeWitt. He kneed his horse toward a lane between two adobes but it was too late, for the officer had seen Steve. DeWitt spoke quickly to Captain Padilla. Padilla saluted and walked off while DeWitt came toward the two boys. Steve slid from his saddle and stood at attention, awaiting DeWitt.

The light-blue eyes were curiously cold as DeWitt returned Steve's salute. " What are you doing here, Ames? " he asked. He glanced quickly at Hernán, then back at Steve. " Have you brought a message to me from Colonel Canby? "

" No, sir."

" Then what are you doing here? "

Steve swallowed. " We came through the mountains east of here from the pass road."

DeWitt looked past Steve toward the hazy purple mountains. " Through there? There is no road."

Hernán flashed his best toothy smile. " *Sí, Capitán,* but we found a way."

" So? On whose orders did you come through there, Ames? "

There was no use in trying to wriggle out of it. " No one gave me orders, sir," said Steve quietly. " I went on my own."

The muscle began to twitch in DeWitt's left cheek. " Come with me," he said sharply. He led the way to a large house at one side of the plaza and entered it. He stood by the fireplace in the low-ceiled living room, with his hands clasped behind his back. A field desk had been set up in the room and it was covered with forms and papers. Several boxes of military impedimenta stood next to the wall, and there was a rack of rusty and pitted muskets near the fireplace. Probably the useless pumpkin-slingers that had been allocated for the defense of New Mexico Territory! They looked as though they would be more dangerous to the shooter than to the target.

" You realize, of course," said DeWitt, " that you are absent without leave? "

" I do not think so," said Hernán brightly. " He lives at home, has no uniform and nothing to do, so — " He stopped short as he saw the look on Steve's face.

DeWitt raised a hand. " It was only through your uncle's say-so that we allowed you to idle your time away in Santa Fe, Ames." He smiled coldly. " It seems as though military discipline comes second after political influence in the territory. It so happened that yesterday I wanted you to ride with me down here to Galisteo and act as translator while we swore in new recruits for the militia company."

" I'm sorry, sir."

" That doesn't matter! There are other things more important than that! Why did you ride out to Glorieta Pass? Why did you come through those mountains? "

" We had an idea we might find those missing wagons, sir."

" So? Patrols from Fort Marcy and Fort Union combed that country looking for them."

Hernán grinned. " It must have been the combs without the teeth, *Capitán!* For we found out where those wagons went! "

DeWitt stared hard at the two boys. " You did? Tell me about it. Not you, Ames, your friend there."

Hernán quickly told the story.

DeWitt motioned to Steve. " Get that rifle you found."

Steve went outside and took the rifle from the cantle pack. He brought it inside. " I thought we might be able to check the serial number of this rifle against the serial list of the rifles that were in the missing wagons, sir," he said.

DeWitt took the weapon and glanced at it. " Yes, perhaps." He looked up. " But you saw no wagons? "

" No, sir."

" You actually think the tracks you saw leaving the pass road were made by the missing wagons? "

Steve shrugged. It was a habit he had acquired from Hernán. *" Quién sabe,* sir? Who knows? "

DeWitt smiled faintly. " Wagon and hoof tracks have no serial numbers, unfortunately for us."

Hernán guffawed, slapping his thighs. " That is a good one, *Señor Capitán!* The *señor capitán* is a wit. I — " Hernán swallowed hard as he saw the frosty look in the officer's eyes.

" Supposing you hadn't met me here, Ames, would you have returned to Santa Fe tomorrow? "

" No, sir," said Steve boldly.

" What would you have done? "

" Gone into the south Galisteo Basin, to find those wagons."

" You think they are there? "

" I'm sure of it, sir."

" You were warned to stay away by that hidden marksman. Weren't you afraid that you might never come back from the Basin? "

" No, sir."

Hernán grinned. " Had you seen Steve shoot that man through the arm, you would not think we are afraid to go into the Basin, *Señor Capitán!* "

DeWitt leaned the rifle against the wall. " Perhaps not. But that is man's work. Have you boys a place to stay here? "

Hernán waved a hand. " There is my Tía Theresa, but she has only two rooms and little to eat."

DeWitt nodded. " There is plenty of room here. Can you forage for your own food? "

" I was a Zouave, sir," said Steve proudly.

" Yes . . . well, do what you can. But one thing! You are leaving for Santa Fe the first thing in the morning. Under orders! I'll take care of the south Galisteo Basin with some of the militiamen we have here."

" Yes, sir! " said Steve.

" Dismissed then! "

The two boys walked outside. Hernán spat into the gutter. " *¡No bueno!* No good! That one makes me ill."

Steve shrugged. " He's right. I had no business leaving Santa Fe. We're lucky he wasn't a little tougher on us."

" He can't hurt Hernán Federico Telesfor Donaciano Gaspar Melchior Calvillo! "

Steve looked surprised. " Who are *they?* " He ducked the wild swing Hernán made at him.

It was dark when they left Tía Theresa's little house at the edge of town near the canal. Steve's money had provided the materials for *cabrito el horno,* in the preparation of which Hernán insisted his Tía Theresa had no equal throughout all Nuevo Mexico, and Steve was inclined to think that Hernán was more a dutiful nephew, rather than a real gourmet.

They stopped near the crumbling tower, built many years ago as protection against the Indians, then allowed to decay in times of peace.

There was a faint tinge of moonlight in the eastern sky, which just served at the time to make the night's darkness seem more intense. Tía Theresa had filled them in on all the activities of Galisteoans from newly born Serafina Velarde to old Pamfilo Ochoa, who was said to be one hundred and two years old, and still cut a fine dancing figure at the local fandangos. She had spoken with pride about Capitán Luis Padilla and his fine company of militiamen, Galisteoans all, who would drive the hated *tejanos* first into the Rio Grande, and then into the Gulf of Mexico, without raising a sweat.

"Tía Theresa knows many things, *amigo*," said Steve.

"That is true."

"She spoke of so much my poor ears are tired."

"That is so."

"She is a veritable mine of information."

"Of a certainty!"

Steve leaned against the side of the tower. "But she said nothing about strangers in the Galisteo Basin. Nothing about strange wagons."

Hernán plucked a stalk of dried grass and thrust it into his mouth. It gave him the look of a wise little burro as he spoke around it. "Tía Theresa not only knows many things, *chico*, which she is willing to tell one and all, but she is also a wise woman who knows when to keep her mouth shut."

Steve nodded. "I had the same feeling, *amigo*." He looked at the eastern sky and the growing moonlight. "But why?"

Hernán chewed at his grass. "It is better to keep one's mouth shut at times. She is a widow with seven children to support. Does it matter to her who has stolen twelve Government wagons? "

" Those stores in the wagons might have helped protect her from the Texans."

" Pah! And does it matter to her whether this territory is ruled by *yanquis* or *tejanos?* Not a whit! "

" But she was afraid of something."

" That is true." Hernán came closer to Steve. " There are men here in Galisteo who do not work too hard at the farming or the woodcutting, yet they always seem to have money. You understand? "

" Yes."

" These wagons. They vanish from the Glorieta Pass road and are spirited through the mountains toward the Galisteo Basin, where they again disappear. Think you not that someone must have seen them? "

" Yes."

Hernán shrugged and held out his hands, palms upward. " If you lived here, a peaceable person, and knew about such things, would you poke your nose into them? "

" I don't know."

" Tía Theresa knows. So do lots of other *paisanos* here in Galisteo. Keep the mouth shut, and the throat does not get slit."

Steve shivered a little in the cold, searching wind that suddenly swept down the street, scattering trash and dry leaves ahead of it. " Let's go to the house," he said. " We can have a fire there."

They walked down the dark street. Galisteo went to bed early behind locked doors and sealed windows. Memories of Jicarilla and Mescalero raids were not too dim in that country.

Captain DeWitt was not in the dark house. The boys went to the room at the rear of the house that he had alloted to them. It was spacious and clean, with a huge and ancient wooden bedstead. Hernán lighted sweet-smelling candles and then lighted the firewood in the beehive fireplace. He squatted on his heels, looking into the dancing flames.

"Of what are you thinking, *hombrecito?*" asked Steve as he took off his jacket and gun belt.

"This Capitán DeWitt. He likes you?"

"I don't think so."

"There is something strange about him."

"How so?" Steve pulled off his boots and dropped onto the bed, resting his chin on his crossed hands so that he could watch the dancing flames.

Hernán shrugged as he took off the serape he had flung across his shoulders. "His mouth says one thing; his eyes say another."

"I agree."

"He is a bitter man, *amigo*."

"That is so."

Hernán spat into the fireplace. "I don't like him," he said with emphasis.

"I wonder who does?"

Hernán turned with a wide grin on his face. "He does!"

Later, as they lay in the huge bed and watched the firelight dance on the low ceiling, Hernán turned to look at Steve. "What will happen when we get back to Santa Fe?"

"*¿Quién sabe?* I'll catch it from Uncle Carter, and you'll have your Tío Eusebio looking for you with a wagon tongue for a switch in his hand."

Hernán shivered a little. "You are in the First New Mexico Volunteers."

Steve sighed. "I was. I don't know what Captain DeWitt will say about me."

"If you are allowed to stay in the regiment, do you think you could find a place for me there?"

Steve hesitated. "Well . . . I think so . . ."

"You do?"

Steve nodded sagely. "They said they needed burros to haul supplies. I think you ought to do nicely, *chico*." Then he ducked under the counterpane to get away from a swinging blow of Hernán's pillow.

It was pitch dark in the big room when Steve awoke at Hernán's tug on his hair. " What is it? " he demanded.

Hernán clasped a hand over Steve's mouth, then placed his mouth close to Steve's left ear. " I went to get a drink of water," he whispered. " On the way back I heard voices in the captain's room at the front of the house. I crept up there and could hear him talking to some man."

Steve removed Hernán's hand from his mouth. " So, what's wrong with that? "

Hernán leaned closer to Steve. " At four o'clock in the morning? "

Steve sat bolt upright, then swung his legs over the side of the bed. " Lead on," he said.

Hernán eased open the bedroom door and led the way toward the big living room at the front of the house. They paused in the hallway. Yellow light shone through the space between the front bedroom door and the side of the doorway.

The voices were muffled, and Steve could not distinguish any words. He started into the living room, but Hernán held him back with a grip of iron.

It was well he did so, for at that instant the door was fully opened and a man came into the living room, a big man wearing a slouch hat, and the lamplight glinted from the silver conches on it. The man turned as he reached the outer door, sharply outlining a hooked nose and a short, ragged beard. " Like I said, Captain, we got everything taken care of down south of here, but it's up to you to do the rest."

" Don't worry about that."

The tall man held a rifle in his left hand and he raised it and shook it. " There's too much at stake now in New Mexico to let anything go wrong."

" I'm well aware of that."

The man grunted. He opened the door and stepped part way through it, then he stopped and looked back. " I still think my way is best. We could do it now."

Milas DeWitt shook his head. " Here . . . in Galisteo? Don't be a fool."

The man laughed shortly. " You don't much like blood, do you, Milas? "

" Not unnecessary blood."

" That may be so! My motto is: *Los muertos no hablan.*"

DeWitt waved a hand as though to brush the man away. " There will be enough blood in New Mexico before long."

" Yes. To win we have to kill. There's no other way, Milas. *Buenas noches, amigo.*"

The man looked quickly both ways and then was gone into the dark night like some demon returning to the nether regions from whence he had come, leaving a reek of sour sweat and stale tobacco smoke behind him as the door closed softly.

Milas DeWitt stood there for a time, outlined in the lighted doorway, and then he struck a fist hard into the palm of his other hand, turned on a heel, and closed the door. In a few minutes the light went out.

The two boys crept back toward their room and as they did so they heard the soft tattoo of hoofs on the earth not far from the house as the mysterious visitor left Galisteo toward the south.

They got into bed. Hernán shivered.

" What's wrong, *amigo?* " asked Steve.

" He was like an *espectro*. A ghost. He made my blood run cold."

" Yes."

" Who was he? I wonder."

" *¿Quién sabe?* "

" You think this Capitán DeWitt is up to something? "

Steve shrugged. " Nothing was said to prove that."

" That is true. What they said could have been considered several ways. Except for one thing, *amigo.*"

" Yes."

" *Los muertos no hablan.*"

Then it was Steve's turn to shiver. *Los muertos no hablan.* The dead do not speak.

CHAPTER

10

Santa Fe, New Mexico Territory,
November, 1861

STEVE AMES opened his eyes and for a moment he was not sure where he was, in his room at Mr. Albright's Academy for Boys and Young Gentlemen in New York, in a tent near Washington, D.C., after Bull Run, or in a house in Galisteo. But then the familiar sight of his own room in his father's house in Santa Fe reassured him.

It must be close to dawn, he thought. It was quiet and yet something had awakened him. In the days since he had come back from Galisteo with Hernán Calvillo, both of them had been in disgrace and Hernán had been hustled off by his Tío Eusebio and his Tía Rosa, while Steve had gotten the reprimand he had expected from Uncle Carter Ames.

Judge Ames had his hands and his mind full enough without worrying about Steve poking about in the Sangre de Cristos while his father was away. The judge's eyes had seemed to spark and flash as he had reproved Steve and Hernán on their return to Santa Fe from Galisteo. Poor Hernán! Not only had he received full blame as well as Steve had from Judge Ames, but Tío Eusebio had used a thick switch, instead of the wagon tongue that Steve had predicted, wielded by a muscular muleteer's arm, on Hernán's shoulders.

Steve shifted in his bed and looked at the dull shine of the silver trumpet hanging over his bed. A lot of water had run under the bridge since the day Dacey Curtis had left the instrument in Steve's charge. There had been little enough Steve could do about using the trumpet to help anyone as Dacey had said it should be used. Now Steve was in trouble, unable to wear his uniform and unable to join his regiment. Confined at home like a little boy. *¡Ay de mí!* He'd hear about that from his messmates when he joined the First New Mexico. It was said they would soon move south to join the Federal forces at Fort Craig. He had pleaded with Uncle Carter to be allowed to join them, but the stern old man had said Steve would stay at home until his father got back from the South, and there had been no word at all from him when he would be back.

There had been one advantage in Steve's confinement. Trumpeter corporal Will Nolan, from Fort Marcy, had heard about the silver trumpet from Judge Ames and had dropped by to see it. He had become so interested in it after he had played it that he had given Steve a manual for trumpet music and had dropped by several evenings to coach Steve in the use of the instrument.

A dull, thudding noise came to Steve. He sat up in bed. Santa Fe, in the dead of the night, was usually as quiet as a tomb.

The thudding noise came again from somewhere near the front of the house. Steve slid from beneath the covers and padded along the hallway to the living room; just as he opened the door into the rain-misted patio he heard the banging on the front gate. He entered the hall and walked to the big door. He placed a hand on the cold metal of the double-barrelled shotgun, which was kept in a niche beside the door for use against unwelcome visitors.

The thumping came again.

"*¿Quién es?*" called out Steve.

" Open up, by the powers! They's two men out here, soaked to the skin, tired, and hungry."

Steve grinned. It was the raucous voice of Luke Comfort. He lifted the bars and swung back the huge door to see two men standing beside horses in the wet street. Steve stared at the man beyond Luke. " Father! " he cried out.

Mark Ames came forward and gripped Steve by the shoulders. " *¡Ay de mí!* " he said. " Look, Luke! He is *mucho hombre* now! Much of the man! "

Steve stared unbelievingly at his father. Beneath the soaked slouch hat his face was thin and drawn, while his poncho seemed to hang on little else than bones and muscles. " What happened to you, Father? You've lost twenty pounds! "

" Twenty-five," said Mark Ames. " Spanish beds and Spanish suppers don't keep meat on a man."

Steve grinned. A Spanish bed was to lie face downward on the harsh earth and pull your back over you for a cover, while a Spanish supper was to tighten one's belt and think of anything else but food.

" What about me? " demanded Luke.

Steve eyed the lean frame of the scout. He was all steel and whang leather, without an ounce of fat on him, and yet he ate like a poor relation at Thanksgiving time.

" Let's get inside," said Mark Ames. He shivered. " We've ridden all night from Galisteo in this drizzle."

They led the tired horses into the patio, and Steve took them to the stable. He took off the cantle and pommel packs, the sheathed rifles, and the wet saddles, and placed them to one side. The horses were all side meat and bones as their masters had been. Steve ran a hand down the neck of his father's horse, and the animal whinnied softly, for he remembered Steve.

Steve rubbed them down and fed them, then carried the rifles into the house. The two men were seated in rawhide chairs, unbooted, while their wet feet, in holey socks, steamed from the heat of the crackling fire. Steve took his father's fine silver-mounted Hawken rifle from the buckskin sheath and hung it on the pegs over the fireplace. The rifle as well as the men and the horses had seen hard service.

"I'll get some forage," said Steve.

"Listen to the soldier," jeered Luke.

Steve grinned at Luke. The scout hadn't changed. He was as timeless as the mountains and deserts he loved. His sharp green eyes peered like those of a predatory bird from each side of his beak of a nose, which itself was slightly askew from some vicious blow in the past. His reddish hair, tinged with gray, hung low on his lean neck, and he wore a raggedly cropped beard.

"Seen enough, *chico?*" asked Luke. "Get the fodder!"

"Where's your uncle?" asked Mark Ames.

"In Taos, sir."

"You're here alone?"

"Yes, sir."

The gray eyes of Mark Ames studied Steve, and it seemed to Steve as though his father knew all about his disgrace before Steve had a chance to open his mouth.

Steve hurried to the kitchen and got food, heaping everything he could find on a tray. He carried it to the living room and placed the food in pots that could be heated beside the fire.

Luke sniffed. "Mexican strawberries," he said.

"Beans," said Steve dryly.

The two men closed their eyes and leaned back in their chairs until the food was ready on the table and then they ate like timber wolves. When they were done Steve poured cups of chocolate for them. It was then that Mark Ames pointed a finger at Steve. "I heard about Galisteo," he said quietly.

"Tía Theresa?"

"Yes."

"I might have known," said Steve.

"Fill us in on the details, son."

Steve told them of the missing wagons and of how Hernán and he had trailed them.

The two men looked at each other. "Who has that rifle now?" asked Mark Ames.

"Oddly enough, sir, when Captain DeWitt returned to Santa Fe, he said someone had stolen it from the house in Galisteo."

"He kept the serial number of course?"

"No."

The two men looked at each other again. "Do you happen to remember the serial number, Steve?" asked Mark Ames.

"No, sir."

Wood crackled in the fire. Steve began to clear the table.

"Would you know the man who visited Captain DeWitt in the middle of the night?" asked his father.

"I think so, sir."

"But you haven't seen him around Santa Fe?"

"I haven't been out of this house, sir, since I got back from Galisteo."

"I see."

"Those wagons never went south of the Galisteo Basin," Luke Comfort said. "They would have been seen."

"It wouldn't be easy to hide twelve big Government wagons," said Steve.

"They could have taken them apart and burned them or scattered the parts."

"There were still twelve teamsters and a few troopers to deal with. They haven't been seen since the wagons were missed."

"They might have been in on the deal."

"And if they weren't?" asked Steve.

The strange green eyes seemed to bore holes into Steve. "*Los muertos no hablan*," said the scout quietly.

Steve refilled the chocolate cups. "What's doing down south?" he asked.

"Too much," said Luke. "Way too much."

Mark Ames sipped his hot chocolate. " After Major Lynde's disgraceful surrender at San Augustine Springs the rebels under Colonel Baylor took possession of the lower valley area from La Mesilla down to El Paso. Rebel troops have been reported forming in San Antonio for the purpose of going on a gigantic 'buffalo hunt,' but we know they are actually three regiments of Texas Mounted Rifles and their purpose is to join Colonel Baylor at La Mesilla and invade northern New Mexico and Arizona too."

Luke nodded sagely. " They got some tough *hombres* leading those three regiments. And they got six mountain howitzers from what we heard."

Steve eyed the scout. " You must have heard a lot."

Mark Ames nodded. " I met Luke at Fort Craig and we rode home together."

" Can Fort Craig hold back the rebels? " asked Steve.

" I think so. They are constructing bombproof buildings and earthworks all about the post. I doubt if the Texans can carry it by assault. But they can pass it."

" Then what happens? "

Steve's father shrugged. " They must fight in the field. Probably at or near Valverde, for it's my guess the Texans will advance up the east side of the Rio Grande and attempt to cross the river at the Valverde Fords, which are upriver from Fort Craig."

" And if the rebels win? "

Luke coughed. " You'll see the Lone Star flag flyin' over Albuquerque, Santa Fe, and maybe even Fort Union."

Mark Ames nodded. " We have the Regulars, of course, and I doubt if the rebels can whip them, but we must also rely on militiamen and volunteers. I can't say that I think much of either type of soldier if you can even call them soldiers."

" I saw some of the Galisteo company of militia," said Steve. He shook his head.

" Supposing the rebels move up the Pecos? " asked Steve.

"Then the troops from Fort Union will have to stop them. I wonder if we'll get volunteer troops from Colorado as the governor requested?"

"Yes," said Steve. "The governor of Colorado has promised them."

"That's a relief!" Mark Ames stood up and paced back and forth. "Señors Gonzalez and Tafolla want to recruit companies in the vicinity of Fort Craig. A Señor Perea wants to recruit a company at large. The Fourth Militia is being recruited at Fort Union and the Fifth at Albuquerque. Señor Alarid plans to form a Santa Fe Company. Señor Mora is ready to organize one at Mora."

Luke Comfort half closed his green eyes. "With the exception of the Fourth and Fifth Militia Regiments, those are all three-months enlistments," he said quietly.

"There were quite a few three-months men at Bull Run," said Steve. He looked at his father. "Some of them started back for Washington just before the battle because their enlistments were up."

Mark Ames nodded. He eyed Steve. "What has your uncle said lately? That is, about the military situation." He grinned at Steve despite his weariness.

"A company of lancers under a Captain Dodd is supposed to be on the way to Santa Fe, *B* Company of the Second Colorado Volunteers. They're to be sent on at once to Fort Craig. The territory is entitled to recruit thirty-two companies of volunteers and militia to replace the Regulars. They wanted to take the Regulars from Canby, but he demanded promised reinforcements from Kansas and Missouri before he'd release the Regulars. He hasn't seen hide nor hair of the Kansas and Missouri men as yet."

"They probably got their own hands full as it is," Luke remarked.

"The whole nation has its hands full," said Mark Ames dryly.

Luke shifted in his seat. "How soon do you want me to go back south, Mark?" he asked.

Steve looked quickly at the scout.

" I'll have to make my confidential report to Governor Connelly and to Canby sometime today," said Mark Ames. " As soon as I know the immediate plans of the territorial government and the military, I'll let you know what we want you to do, Luke."

Luke shrugged. *" 'Stá bueno,"* he said.

" I'm going to get some sleep," said Steve's father. " Call me no later than eight o'clock." He slapped Steve on the shoulder and then left the room.

Luke fiddled with his chocolate cup. " I'd like to get out of here as quickly as possible."

" You just got back, Luke."

" You know how I hate walls and houses around me."

" Yes. What will you do when they send you down there? "

Luke winked. " Use my nose, ears, and eyes."

" Spying? "

Luke laughed. " That ain't nice! I'm a scout! A civilian employee, son! "

" What's the difference? "

Luke made a motion around his lean neck with a finger, then jerked a hand up while at the same time he tilted his head sideways, thrust out his tongue, and goggled his eyes.

There was no need for words. Steve shivered a little. He remembered only too well what had happened to a peddler in the military camps outside of Washington who had asked too many questions and had been in too many places where he had had no business being.

Luke studied Steve closely. " You've changed a lot," he said. " Filled out. Something different about you too. Like you suddenly stopped being a boy and are getting to be a man."

" I learned a lot at Bull Run, Luke."

The scout nodded. He leaned back in his chair. " Took a heap of nerve to follow that trail through the Sangre de Cristos too."

" I got tired of sitting around here."

" I had a chance to talk to your *compañero* . . . Hernán Calvillo."

" How is he? " asked Steve eagerly.

Luke grinned. " Still sore about the shoulders. His Tío Eusebio is a big, strong man. Hernán wanted to come back with us and join the army, but your father talked him out of it." The green eyes became speculative. " From what he tells me you did a good job of tracking those wagons."

" It wasn't much, Luke."

Luke waggled a finger. " Mebbe so, mebbe not. Fact is you was the only ones who had any idea of where they went."

Steve nodded gloomily. " By now they've vanished completely! If Captain Milas DeWitt had let us go after them, we might have learned more."

Luke nodded.

" When he came back to Santa Fe he said nothing about the militia company of Captain Padilla going to look for them."

" Fact is, Steve, he never sent them."

Steve stared at Luke. " You're sure? "

" Positive."

" But that was loco! They were in the Galisteo Basin! Where else could they have gone? "

" Aye, indeed, where else? "

" I wonder about him sometimes."

Luke looked into the dying fire. " I wonder about a lot of so-called patriots in this territory. We've lost a number of United States Army officers to the rebels."

" Nothing really wrong with that, Luke. The rebel armies in the east are full of them. They resigned because they believed in state's rights."

Luke leaned forward. " Aye! I've got nothing against *them!* But the war started last April! This is November and soon to be December! Seven months have passed since Fort Sumter was fired upon, and there are still men in the uniform of the United States Army who are rebels at heart. They're waiting to see how much damage they can do before they finally put on a gray suit! Men in high positions! Not second and first lieutenants but colonels and brigadier generals, no less! "

"Do you think Captain DeWitt is one of them?" asked Steve quietly.

Luke cut a hand sharply sideways. "I didn't say that! Milas DeWitt has worked hard for Canby. He's saved him from a lot of bother for one thing."

Steve nodded. "I know that for sure," he said dryly.

"He's a West Pointer, which don't mean too much as far as his politics go. But he knows this country and the people. He hasn't let anything stand in the way of his duty."

"No," said Steve. They really had nothing on the man. "Except for one thing, Luke, he's all right in your book."

The green eyes seemed to harden like emeralds. "So?"

"You don't like him."

Luke's tanned face suddenly changed. He laughed loudly and slapped his hands on his hard thighs. "Aye!"

Steve smiled. "Hernán Calvillo says one person likes him."

"Who?"

"Himself."

"That is so! Hernán is no fool."

Steve placed more wood on the fire. "When you go south again," he asked quietly, "will you go alone?"

"I suppose so."

"But you wouldn't mind having a *compañero?"*

"No," said Luke.

"Luke, would you take me with you?"

"You'll have to have your father's permission."

"I know that."

"Ask him then. If he says, '*Está bueno,*' then you can ride with old Luke Comfort."

"Gracias, Luke. *¡Gracias!"*

Luke waved a hand. " It is nothing, *amigo.* I was going to ask him anyway."

Steve paced back and forth. " I know that country! I know the people! My father showed me the trails and the water holes. I can be of real help. I can see like a hawk, Luke, and shoot as good as most men. You won't be sorry. We'll do a good job."

A gentle snore interrupted Steve. The scout was already sound asleep.

CHAPTER

II

Santa Fe, New Mexico Territory,
December, 1861

THE WIND blew through the quartermaster warehouse and set the lamps and candles to guttering. It moaned about the adobe walls and whispered through the cracks in the thick shutters.

Steven Ames looked up from the tall desk at which he stood, beyond the pool of yellow light from his lamp, and eyed the serried ranks of bales, bags, boxes, and heaps of equipment that almost completely filled the warehouse.

Major Donaldson was at the far end of the warehouse with his chief quartermaster clerk, and Steve could hear their voices although he could not distinguish the words. But the two men were worried.

Steve looked again at the two lists lying before him. It had been his misfortune early in his schooling to reveal that he wrote a fine copperplate hand, and when Donaldson had mentioned in Steve's father's hearing that he needed clerks at the big quartermaster warehouse, it had been sufficient for Steve to be practically sentenced to the job.

He hadn't been long at his task when he had learned that there were some serious shortages in the supplies that had been moved from Fort Union down to Santa Fe for eventual transshipment to Fort Craig. Now, for two days and part of the cold evenings, he had been at his desk while Major Donaldson and Quartermaster Sergeant Nye went carefully through the drafty warehouse, checking and re-checking, and as yet they had not been able to find the shortages.

Santa Fe was a place of thieves, and in fact New Mexico Territory had a lot more than its share of them. The people were poor, more like slaves in many ways than free citizens of the United States. In fact it had been said that the average Negro slave lived far better than did many of the peons of New Mexico. So, in order to live, they stole anything they could lay their hands on. But the warehouse was well guarded by Regulars from Fort Marcy. The windows were small and strongly barred. It was a hard nut for a thief to crack.

Steve shivered a little in the draft. He hunched his caped army overcoat higher on his shoulders and thought with longing of the bright fire that would be burning in the big living room at home.

He copied a few more lines in his flowing hand, but his mind wandered off to the war. News trickled in from the East, some of it true and some of it false, and a man could digest it and come out with his own conclusions. There had been a few small engagements in Virginia. The Union forces had lost the battle of Wilson's Creek in Missouri. Lexington, Missouri, had been captured by the rebel General Price with the loss of the entire Chicago Irish Brigade. There had been a few actions in West Virginia at Cross Lanes, Gauley Mountain, and Buffalo Hill. A rebel general by the name of Robert E. Lee had done a little timid moving about Elk Water with raw troops and had accomplished absolutely nothing. General George Brinton McClellan was reorganizing the Union army in the vicinity of Washington and had promised the capture of Richmond in the spring.

In New Mexico things had moved along. Luke Comfort

had left for the south without Steve Ames. Colonel Canby had been promoted to the command of the newly formed Department of New Mexico. The rebel general Sibley, with his Texas Mounted Rifles, was said to be at Fort Bliss in Texas, ready for the invasion of New Mexico. Federal troops were being concentrated at Fort Craig to resist that invasion under Canby's command. One of his regiments was the First New Mexico Volunteer Infantry under the command of Kit Carson, and they lacked one drummer by the name of Steven Ames.

The major came back through the warehouse and stopped beside Steve's desk. "I hope you've found some discrepancies," he said.

"Nothing, sir."

Donaldson nodded glumly. "I had little faith that you would. This beats me."

"How much is missing, sir?"

The officer checked a list he held in his hand. "Not a great deal of one item, it seems. Rather, an assortment of items. Rifle caps, medicines, Enfield carbines, some sabers, a great many pistols, powder, and lead. Items we can hardly do without for this coming campaign in the south."

"Have you any idea what might have happened to them?"

Donaldson shrugged. "Those two lists you have there should check out. One of them was a list sent here from Fort Union, the other is the list made out by Captain Florian, whom I relieved some months ago." The officer looked toward the rear of the warehouse. "Florian was a poor man for quartermaster, but his records seemed to be accurate when I took over. One thing bothers me though."

"Yes, sir?"

"Before I took over as quartermaster there were some shipments made to the south. To a large depot in Albuquerque and to smaller depots in Peralta, Belen, and a few others down south. I know those shipments were made, yet we have no records of all that material reaching those depots."

The candles guttered in the draft. The wind seemed to moan a little louder. Papers fluttered on the desk.

Donaldson struck his hands sharply together. " Some of that material never reached its destination."

" Like the wagons that were lost in Glorieta Pass last October? "

The major looked quickly at Steve. " Why do you say that? "

Steve shrugged. " They just seemed to vanish."

" Near Galisteo."

" Yes, sir."

Donaldson paced back and forth. " Some of the shipments we sent south went by way of Bernalillo and others went by way of Galisteo." He rubbed his lean jaws. " Sergeant Nye! " he called out.

The quartermaster soldier came through the gloom of the warehouse. " Yes, sir? " he asked.

" Check through your records. Is there any way you can tell which of those shipments since this spring went through Bernalileo and which went via Galisteo?"

Nye took his lower lip between his teeth for a moment. Then he looked up. " By heaven, sir," he said quietly. " There's no need for me to check that at all! "

" Go on! "

Nye looked up at the low ceiling as though concentrating. "The only reason we sent shipments via Galisteo was because of a bad Indian scare near Bernalillo. I mind it well, because I thought it was an old wives' tale. But it was said that Navahos in great numbers had been seen near Bernalillo and so some shipments went via Galisteo, although the weather was bad and the road was almost impassable in places. I remembered something odd the other day when we began to suspect that these supplies were missing. The shipments we had sent via Bernalillo all got through safely, while what we sent via Galisteo were the ones that had the missing items."

" You're sure of that? "

" Yes, sir."

" Why didn't you tell me before now? "

The sergeant looked surprised. " I didn't think it mattered that much, sir! All I knew was that the items were missing, and it didn't seem to matter whether they had been sent either way."

Donaldson nodded. " That's true, Nye. This we know: the items are not here, nor are they in any of the depots south of here, therefore they must have disappeared on the way."

" It's possible, sir," said the noncom. " After all, they went down by civilian transport, not by army wagons."

" What's that, Nye? "

" Its quite customary, sir, as you know."

Steve nodded. " My father used to contract quite a lot to haul Government goods and materials. But not at that time, Major."

Donaldson waved a hand. " Your father and his employees are above suspicion, young man." He looked at Nye. " Find out for me who contracted for those shipments and who hauled them."

" Yes, sir."

" I want a full report in the morning."

Donaldson took out his watch. " Nine o'clock! " he said with a surprised look on his face. " You're dismissed, young Ames." He look steadily at Steve. " I think it hardly necessary to remind you that all you have heard here in the past few minutes is not to go beyond this warehouse."

" No, sir."

" Good night, then."

Steve took his forage cap and put it on. He saluted the officer, then left the warehouse. The cold wind seemed to carry a warning of snow in it. He looked down the slope toward the quiet city and its twinkling yellow lights. Behind him he could hear call to quarters being played on the bugle at Fort Marcy, while below him was the diamond-shaped Garita with its towers, built originally for Spanish prisoners condemned to be hanged and now used by the army as a guardhouse.

He walked down the windy hill and as he did so he looked to the south through the darkness beyond the city. Somewhere down there his regiment, with which he had never served, was at Fort Craig waiting for the enemy advance.

He passed through the dark cold streets and as he reached the vicinity of his father's house he saw a figure seated near the outer gate, swathed in a serape and with a great steeple-crowned hat on its head. Steve hesitated. The streets of Santa Fe usually held a swarm of beggars, but no beggar would be out on a night as cold as this. Steve slid a hand inside his overcoat and gripped the butt of his navy Colt.

The figure moved. "*Hola, amigo,*" it said.

"Hernán! What are you doing here?"

Hernán's teeth chattered violently before he could speak. "Let us go inside," he said. "I am cold and hungry. The rabbits have their burros and the birds have their nests, but Hernán Federico Telesfor Donaciano Gaspar Melchior Calvillo has no place to lay his head."

Steve glanced sideways at his friend as he unlocked the small door. Every time Hernán showed up there was trouble, and yet life was a little empty around Santa Fe without the irrepressible apprentice muleteer.

Later, after they had eaten, the sad-eyed Hernán told Steve what had happened. "My uncle joined the militia, Steve. He was sent south to Soccoro to guard the stores there with his company — Capitán Padilla's. On the way my uncle was thrown from his mule and badly hurt. My Tía Rosa hurried at once to be with him. I stayed in the house for a week and I got lonely for my friend Steve."

Steve refilled their chocolate cups. "I am glad you came, *amigo,*" he said quietly.

Hernán eyed Steve's uniform. "Can you get me into the army?"

"Can you play a drum?"

Hernán sadly shook his head.

" Then I'll teach you."

Hernán looked at Steve. " But you, why are you not with the First New Mexico? They are at Fort Craig, waiting to fight the rebels. Are you not in a hurry to join them? "

Steve shrugged. " Certainly I am! But I'm stuck here in Santa Fe, fighting with pen and ink instead of with powder and ball, and every time I open my mouth around my father or uncle they tell me a soldier serves where he is ordered to serve and keeps his mouth shut no matter where else he wants to be."

Hernán nodded gloomily. " How can they expect the war to be won here in New Mexico without us? "

Steve stood up and paced back and forth. " There is something we can do."

" So? "

" Those wagons we tracked down to the Galisteo Basin were never found."

" That is so."

Steve quickly told him of what had happened in the big quartermaster warehouse that evening.

Hernán's sad eyes lighted up. " It seems as though there is a big hole in the air where wagons and stores vanish," he said thoughtfully. " Right near Galisteo."

They looked at each other and then they both grinned. " Where is El Diablo? " asked Steve suddenly.

" Tía Rosa tried to ride him south to where my uncle is, but you know El Diablo. She came back afoot and got a burro. I haven't seen El Diablo since. I walked from Galisteo."

" We'll get a horse for you."

" Like El Diablo? "

Steve held out his hands, palms upward. " Where in the world would there be another El Diablo? "

" That is so! " Hernán emptied his chocolate cup. " But you are on duty here in Santa Fe. Remember what happened the last time you left here without permission."

Steve nodded. " Tomorrow is Sunday. I'm not expected for duty. That will give us a whole day."

" But it is twenty-three miles to Galisteo! By the time we get there, poke our noses into places to learn things, then ride back here, it would be at least Tuesday."

Steve nodded. " Still, I feel that we can do more good down there than we can here."

" Maybe we'll meet Captain DeWitt again."

" He's at Fort Union, *amigo.*"

Hernán grinned. " This is a happy coincidence! When do we leave? "

" Tonight."

Hernán's face fell. " I knew it! I find a hot fire, warm food, a good bed to sleep in, then I have to leave."

Steve grinned back at Hernán. " You wanted to be a soldier, *amigo*. A soldier serves where he is ordered to serve and keeps his mouth shut no matter where else he wants to be."

Hernán rolled his eyes upwards. " *¡Madre mía!* " he said piously. " We have here the philosopher."

" You can always stay here. I'm sure my father and uncle can find something for you to do, Hernán — such as cleaning out the stables."

Hernán nodded solemnly. " There is salt in what you say." He slapped Steve on the back. " I will get the horses. Which one shall be mine? "

" The sorrel mare."

" No stallion? "

" Not like El Diablo," said Steve sorrowfully.

Hernán shrugged. " I will lose face riding the sorrel mare, but it is true that I would not care to walk back to Galisteo tonight."

" *Vámonos* then!"

The wall clock softly chimed eleven strokes.

Chapter

12

Galisteo Basin, New Mexico Territory,
December, 1861

IT WAS DAWN when Steve Ames drew rein and looked back at Hernán. They had ridden a good part of the night, resting now and then, until they had bypassed sleeping Galisteo. Steve wanted to take no chances on being found out as they had been the last time they had come to the Galisteo area.

Hernán was muffled in his serape and had a blanket tied about his waist Indian style. "*¡Está frío!*" he said with chattering teeth.

"It is cold," said Steve. He looked ahead through broken country. In the gray distance he could see a mountain range. He had no idea what they were looking for, but if those missing wagons had been taken to the Galisteo Basin and never seen again, there must be some trace of them left somewhere. "What's ahead, *amigo?*" he asked.

Hernán stood up in his stirrups and peered from beneath the broad rim of his battered hat. He smiled thinly. "There is a ruined adobe not far from here. When I was hunting with Tío Eusebio one time we stayed the night there."

They rode on with the keening wind knifing through their clothing until they saw the ruins. It had been a small adobe, probably used by simple and poverty-stricken people, but they had had a view that was priceless. To the south was a panoramic spread, still dulled by the retreating night, but with the sun up, it would be magnificent.

They led the tired horses into a rock-walled corral at the rear of the crumbling house, and scattered food for them on a broad, wooden cart bed that lay there. They hung blankets over the horses, then carried their saddlebags into the house.

The kitchen wasn't in bad repair, although there were holes in the earthen roof. Hernán worked quickly to gather dry juniper and piñon wood while Steve got out the food. In a short time a smokeless fire was crackling in the fireplace. The boys placed a spider over the glowing coals and filled it with bacon. In a little while they were munching bacon sandwiches and gulping thick chocolate.

While Hernán cleaned the spider and the chocolate pot, Steve walked outside and looked down into the great basin below the house. The sun was just tipping the eastern mountains, with a promise of warmth, but it was still cold in the basin. Steve uncased his uncle's field glasses and began to scan the terrain with them. There was little to see until the sun rose higher. Hernán came up behind Steve. "Just what are we looking for, *chico?*" he asked.

"I don't really know."

Hernán rested his elbows on the wall. "If I were hiding stolen goods," he said, "I would place them in the Espectro Valley."

Steve turned. "Ghost Valley?"

"*Sí*. It is a strange place. Many years ago the Indians, Tewas I think, lived there and then they left. Then the Spaniards came and in time there was a little mission and chapel there, but the Indians fought with them, and there was a drought followed by a massacre, so the good padres did not go there again. In the years that followed people tried to live there, but one way or another, they were driven away."

" Driven? "

Hernán shrugged. " *¿Quién sabe?* All I know is that it is not a good place. My people will not go there. There is a curse upon the place."

Steve peered through the glasses.

" But you will go? " asked Hernán uneasily.

" Yes."

" Alone."

" Do I have to? "

There was a moment's silence and then Hernán spoke. " It is true that I am afraid, but I am more afraid that you would think I had no honor by not going with you."

Steve grinned. " I need a guide, *compañero*."

" You have one, *hombrecito*."

" Let's get some sleep then."

Hernán shook his head. " Who can sleep thinking about going to the Espectro Valley? You sleep, *amigo*. I will stand guard."

Steve cased the glasses and handed them to his companion, then he went into the ruin, wrapped himself in his blankets and army overcoat, and closed his eyes. He was worried. He was absent without leave again, but nothing seemed to have been done about tracing down those missing wagons and the supplies that had disappeared so mysteriously some months before the wagons had vanished. He fell asleep thinking about the praise that he and his companion would get when they solved the mystery of the Galisteo Basin.

The sun was up high, driving some of the chill from the air, but there was still a cold wind searching through the valley. Hernán stopped leading his horse and pointed down the valley. " There is a ruin," he said. " Once it belonged to the Casias family. There was a Jicarilla raid. None of the Casias were left. That was a long time ago."

They led the horses along the side of the valley away from the sweeping wind. Steve eyed the ground. There was a faint, rutted road through the valley, but it looked as though it had not been used for many years.

The old Casias house and buildings were nothing but heaps of crumbled adobe and rock with a straggling thatch of brush upon them.

It was a lonely place. Hernán was obviously nervous, while time and time again Steve found himself looking quickly back along the valley as though someone was following them, although there was no sign of life. Then, too, there was the constant feeling that they were being watched. There was no proof of this, for they could see no one, no movements of man or animal and yet the feeling was still there.

It was late afternoon when Steve halted and stared at the heights to the east of the valley.

"What is it, Steve?" asked Hernán.

"I thought I saw smoke."

"Up there? There is no smoke, for there is no one to make it." Hernán looked at the sun. "It will be dark before we leave this accursed place."

Steve looked at him. "We haven't found anything yet."

Hernán shivered a little. "If we stay here, someone will find us."

"There are other ruins east of us?"

"Yes."

"We could shelter there for the night."

"*¿Está loco?* Have you reason or mind? Men have come in here and have never been seen again. None of my people would, or would any Indian come in here and stay the night."

Steve grinned. "Only a loco Anglo like me, eh, *chico?*"

Hernán swallowed as he looked past Steve. "Look," he said hoarsely.

Steve turned and looked at the broken land to the east. A thread of smoke was rising until it met the unseen current of the wind and then it was tattered and driven from sight. " What is it? " he asked, almost to himself. " Not Indians for certain."

They walked on until they reached a slope, which they ascended, and then they could look down into a place where the valley narrowed. Steve stared at some low-lying buildings, half concealed by brush and trees. They looked almost like features of the terrain itself. There was a tower there, with gaping windows, rising above a crumbling ruin. The place looked fearfully alone in the dying sunlight.

" It is the old mission, I think," said Hernán. He crossed himself quickly.

Steve led the way, but this time he held his carbine ready. The sun was almost gone when they reached the crumbling rock and adobe fence that enclosed the mission and the outbuildings.

The wind moaned through the bell tower and fluttered the dry trees and brush.

" No one comes here," said Hernán. " Not even the animals. It is a place of the dead."

Steve handed the reins of Zouave to his companion, then swung a leg over the fence. He crossed the littered churchyard, between the rows of ancient, sagging crosses of gray wood, until he stood at last upon the low flagstone platform at the entrance to the chapel. Yards of plaster had fallen from the old walls. Here and there seemed to be the pocks of bullets that had struck the thick walls. Brush shrouded the base of the structure.

He walked into the building and stopped as his steps echoed through the cold nave. The very silence seemed heavy in the place. There was a doorway to his right, cut through a thick wall, and he entered into a smaller room, the baptistry. There was a stairway built into the walls of the tower itself, and he ascended it, feeling with a free hand ahead of him while his boot soles crunched on fallen plaster and debris.

He stopped at the top, in the place where the bells hung.

There was only one of them left, a thick-shelled bell, green with age. He flicked a fingernail against it and the soft sweet tone of the bell seemed to linger in the air.

Steve looked to the east, through the openings, and saw the heights still lighted with the last rays of the dying sun. For a moment he stared. There was a yellow fleck of light against the reddened rock of the heights. He shook his head and stared again. A tendril of smoke rose from the vicinity of the light and then vanished in the wind.

Steve walked to the other side of the tower and looked down upon Hernán, who stood rooted to the exact spot where Steve had left him. Hernán Federico Telesfor Donaciano Gaspar Melchior Calvillo had courage all right. Steve wondered how many of his people would stand there in a so-called haunted valley while a friend prowled through a long-abandoned church.

Steve looked again to the east. The light had vanished. But someone had lighted a fire or a lamp over there. Who was it?

He went down the stairs and glanced toward the sanctuary, now shrouded in darkness. The stations of the cross had been defaced, and the floor of the nave was littered with filth and debris. A sad fate for a place of worship.

Steve left the echoing pile and walked across to Hernán. The sun was gone. "Come on," said Steve.

Hernán swallowed. He cast one more desperate look behind him, toward the west, where he wanted to be, then led the horses along the fence until he found an opening.

Steve found a low building that would at least keep the cold night wind from reaching them. They had cooked enough food that morning so that they might have a cold supper that night. Hernán ate silently, then wrapped himself in his serape and blankets. "There will be a moon tonight," he said at last. He peered at Steve. "Enough to see the trail to Galisteo."

Steve did not answer. He himself wanted to leave this echoing place of the dead, but something kept him there.

He felt as though the riddle of the missing wagons and supplies could be answered there. How, or when, he did not know, but he had a feeling deep within him that he was right.

The moon was well up, bathing the quiet and rugged terrain in a silvery wash of light. The mission looked as though it were carved from alabaster in the soft light.

Hernán was sound asleep. Steve covered his companion with the blanket he himself no longer needed, and padded softly from the room. There was no light on the eastern slopes of the valley. To Steve's knowledge, there were no roads up in that country, and hardly any trails.

He walked past a long building that had collapsed into a heap of rubble until he reached a stout building, set back against a natural wall of rock. The door was intact. He tested it, but it would not budge. There was no lock, so the door might be wedged shut by debris. He went on toward the rear of the building to a window that was shuttered. He pried open the edge of one shutter with his sheath knife and worked his way into the building.

He stood there for quite a while until his eyes became accustomed to the dimness. The room was littered with rough broken furniture, shards of glass and pottery, partly burned faggots of wood, broken boxes, and torn sacks. The air was dead in the big room. Steve walked across to the fireplace, wishing there were a roaring fire in it, and as he did so his foot struck something that rustled. He bent to pick up a crumpled newspaper. Taking it to the window he saw that it was a copy of the Mesilla *Times,* a definitely pro-Southern sheet, dated late in October. The *Times* was known to flourish under the protection of Colonel Baylor, who had captured Lynde's command at San Augustine Springs.

How had that paper come to be there? He folded it and placed it inside his coat. This was an out-of-the-way place, scarcely the place to find such a newspaper. He looked about until he found a stub of candle, which he lighted.

The flickering light glinted from something in a corner, and he picked it up. It was an officer's shoulder strap with the twin silver bars of a captain's insignia on the blue material. It didn't look as though it had been there very long.

There was a door just behind the filthy fireplace. He tried the door and it gave just a little. He threw his shoulder against it, and it gave a little more until he could get a purchase between the edge of the door and the doorway with a piece of broken timber. He walked into the room and raised the candle. He whistled softly. The room was piled with sacks and boxes from one end to the other. He took out his knife and slit the end sack. A thin trickle of flour came from it. He walked along the line of boxes. The place reminded him of the quartermaster warehouse in Santa Fe, and what was more, the bags and boxes were all stamped U.S.

He reached the end of the long room. There were barrels piled up there and they too were stamped with the letters U.S. Beyond them was a rack of rifles. He leaned closer to the rack. New rifles. Issue .58 caliber Springfields. Behind the rack were sets of equipment, cartridge and cap boxes, sheathed bayonets, and pistol holsters.

Steve walked slowly back to the first room. There was no sign of life in that isolated valley. They had seen nothing but that mysterious thread of smoke to the east, and the faint yellow light he had seen just after sunset. Yet here in this long-abandoned building was a small fortune in Government supplies. As he walked into the first room he slid a hand inside his coat to touch the folded newspaper. The Mesilla *Times*.

Steve blew out the candle and walked to the window by which he had entered. He climbed outside and started for the building in which Hernán was sleeping.

He saw Hernán standing near the front of the church. Steve grinned. His *amigo* was still scared and probably wanted to get out of there while they had moonlight to show the way.

"Hernán!" he called.

Hernán turned and beckoned to him. The boy had his carbine in his hands.

Steve walked quickly. " I found the supplies! " he said.

Hernán turned and the moonlight fell on his face. Steve stopped short, and ice seemed to course through his veins. Hernán seemed a foot taller than he really was, and now he had a great hooked nose and a ragged beard.

The carbine snapped up and flashed, just ten feet from Steve, and the yellow spurt of flame half blinded him at the same instant a sledge-hammer blow struck his left shoulder and drove him back against the church.

" Steve! Steve! " It was the voice of Hernán and it seemed to come from a great distance.

Steve looked up at the bearded man and he knew him. The man looked toward the building where Hernán had slept. There was a splash of yellow fire from the building and the slam of a slug against the church wall inches from the bearded man. He darted around to the front of the church, and a moment later came the hard tattoo of hoofs on the rocky ground.

Steve raised himself on one elbow to see Hernán running toward him, ramming home a charge in his Enfield carbine. The boy had saved his life. Steve opened his mouth. " Hernán . . . I . . ."

" I will stay with you, *amigo!* Never fear! " called out Hernán stoutly.

It was the last thing Steve remembered.

Chapter 13

Santa Fe, New Mexico Territory, February, 1862

"TRY IT AGAIN, Stevie," said Trumpeter Corporal Will Nolan. He leaned back in his chair and closed his eyes.

Steve Ames eased his bandaged shoulder, hitched himself up a little in his bed, then placed the silver trumpet to his lips. The lilting notes of the charge came from the beautiful instrument. Steve half closed his eyes. He could conjure up a picture of Dacey Curtis that day long ago at Bull Run, when the First Virginia Cavalry had smashed the Eleventh New York Volunteers into ruin. Then the silver trumpet had seemed to shriek in joy, high above the crash of the battle, like a screaming, wheeling eagle.

The silvery notes died away, and Steve came back to reality. He looked at the trumpeter.

Nolan nodded his head. " Fine," he said.

Hernán poked his head into the bedroom, " *¡'Stá bueno!* " he agreed. "I have soup for you, *amigo*."

Nolan stood up and put on his forage cap. "You're the best I've heard on the charge, Steve. Seems as though some trumpeters have certain calls they never master and some they can play better than anyone else. I'll say this: I've never heard anyone play that call, the charge, like you can, Steve."

Hernán smiled proudly as he placed the tray on a table, then his smile faded as he saw the look on Steve's face.

Steve passed a chamois cloth up and down the instrument. "You weren't at Bull Run, Will," he said to the trumpeter. "No matter who plays the silver trumpet from now on, no one will ever play it like Dacey Curtis did that day."

Nolan buttoned his caped overcoat. "An odd story, that."

Steve nodded.

Nolan eyed Steve. "You'll be up and about soon no doubt?"

"Yes."

"Good-by then."

"*Adiós, amigo.*"

The soldier left the room and a moment later the two boys heard the outer door close. Steve eyed the soup. He was sick of being an invalid, and yet no matter how foul his humor was it seemed he could do nothing to rile Hernán.

Hernán began to straighten up the room. "Your father and uncle are at the Governor's Palace," he said. "There is a rumor that the Texans are advancing north along the Rio Grande Valley."

Steve looked up quickly. "Do they say there will be a battle?"

"*¿Quién sabe?* Our forces cannot let them get north of Fort Craig. It is said they hope to capture the Valverde Fords."

"That figures. Listen! Go up town and see what you can learn."

"*¡Sí!*"

When Hernán was gone Steve got out of bed. He had been feeling fit for days, but Doctor Dunlap had kept him confined as though he was a child. Steve still suspected the good doctor had done so upon orders from Steve's father.

He dressed quickly, putting on his uniform. It was the first time he had donned it since that day, weeks ago, when he and Hernán had left for Galisteo. The memory of the trip from Espectro Valley back to Galisteo under the care of Hernán was nothing but a painful blur to Steve. Luckily, there had been an army ambulance at Galisteo that had taken Steve at once to Santa Fe, with Hernán sitting up beside him all the way. That trip, too, was merely a mist in Steve's mind.

Steve put on his caped overcoat and buttoned it. The worst part of the whole escapade, as their dangerous trip had been labeled, was that absolutely nothing had come of it. In the confusion of getting Steve to Santa Fe, Hernán had garbled up the story of their findings in Espectro Valley. But it was true that Hernán had not seen the stores, and he himself had found it hard to believe Steve's story. His chief concern, laudable enough, had been to get Steve to safety. Later, when Steve had spoken about what he had found, the story was treated as delirium coupled with a desire to cover up for what was a second serious breach of discipline by Steve.

Steve brushed off his neat forage cap, with its polished brass infantry trumpet insignia pinned to the crown, and placed it on his head. He put the silver trumpet inside its cloth case, then took it to its storage place in the old rosewood piano.

The only person who had listened to Steve had been Major Donaldson, and through his instigation, a cavalry detail from Fort Marcy had ridden at last to Galisteo under the command of Captain Milas DeWitt. That had been another fiasco for Steve, for DeWitt had reported that there was nothing but ruins in the valley and certainly no sign of purloined military stores. Still Major Donaldson, a busy man, had covered up for Steve by saying that Steve had had his permission to ride to Galisteo. He had meant to pursue the search still further, but the war had caught up with the entire Department of New Mexico by that time. Headquarters had been moved to Fort Craig, near the Valverde Fords.

There had been some lively little skirmishes down south. Captains Mink and Vidall and their commands had been captured at Canada Alamosa. The score had been evened by the capture of a captain and nine men from Baylor's Second Regiment of Texas Mounted Rifles. Both Union and Confederate forces had many fights with raiding Indians, and some wit had said that it would be better if the New Mexicans and Texans joined forces to wipe out the Indians so that the white men could get on with their own private war in peace and quiet.

Steve walked out into the dark cold patio. He hunched into the collar of his coat as he went toward the plaza. It seemed as though everything he had done since he had come home to New Mexico had been wrong. His father and uncle worked like Trojans for the territory, with little time for Steve and his problems. His father had donned the uniform of a staff officer working with the territorial government. Many officers and enlisted men whom Steve had known and seen around Santa Fe had been sent south to Fort Craig, and among them was Captain Milas DeWitt. He was due for promotion it was said, nothing less than a colonelcy. Steve felt as though he had done the man an injustice by being so suspicious of him. Milas DeWitt had worked hard for the defense of the territory and had insisted on being assigned to Fort Craig when he, with a major's rank, could very well have stayed in Santa Fe and out of the way of rebel Minie balls.

Strength had been coming to New Mexico in dribbles and drabbles. Some Colorado Volunteers, Pike's Peakers, had been sent to Fort Craig, while others were said to be on their way to Fort Union and thence to Santa Fe or farther south if needed.

The territorial legislature had convened in Santa Fe in January, and it soon had become evident that Union men had the majority, for one of the first acts in the Session of 1862 was to repeal an act entitled "An Act Providing for the Protection of Slave Property in this Territory," which had been passed by the legislature on February 3, 1859. Repeal of the law of 1859 demonstrated that New Mexico Territory had reversed itself on the slavery question and let the world know that New Mexico had firmly allied itself with the Union cause. One of the members of the legislature who had fought wholeheartedly for the repeal had been Steve's uncle, Carter Ames.

There were few people in the wind-swept plaza. Steve wandered over to the Governor's Palace to see if he could pick up some news, but the place was almost deserted. An orderly nodded to Steve. "Feeling better?" he asked.

Steve grinned ruefully. "I feel better than I did before I stopped that piece of lead."

The orderly smiled. "That was one part of your story that was proved to be true. You did get shot."

Steve flushed. He started for the door and saw a pile of luggage and boxes beside it, topped by some uniforms on hangers. "Who's moving out?" he asked.

The orderly looked up. "That's Captain DeWitt's stuff. I was told to clean out his room and send that stuff up to Fort Marcy for storage. Guess he'll be busy for a time down at Fort Craig, and they need his room."

Steve eyed the top uniform blouse. It wasn't a new one and seemed to have seen a lot of service. The lamplight shone on the brass buttons and on one of the shoulder tabs. Steve moved closer to the uniform. The right-hand shoulder tab's color was dull, the gilt faded and greenish from much exposure to the elements, but the left-hand shoulder tab was much brighter and of a slightly different pattern.

"Watch the door," said the orderly. "I'm going to get me a cup of coffee."

Steve was alone in the room. He moved the lamp to a table beside the pile of luggage and uniforms and studied the two shoulder tabs. There wasn't any doubt that the two tabs were not exact mates. He thrust a hand into his overcoat pocket and drew out the tab he had found in the building the night he had been shot. He placed it beside the older tab on the uniform. It was an exact mate in color, texture, and size.

Footsteps sounded in the hallway. Steve placed the lamp on the orderly's desk and stepped back. The orderly entered the room. "Thanks, Steve," he said. "Cold and getting colder. They say there's snow up around Raton Pass and they expect a blizzard. Rough on the Colorado boys."

"How so?"

"The First Colorado Volunteers are on the way down here, it's said."

Steve nodded. He had hardly heard what the orderly had said. He walked out into the cold night. A shoulder tab was hardly enough to incriminate a gentleman and an officer in the crime of stealing Government property, and on top of that, Steve was hardly in a position to accuse anyone of such a thing, not after the two messes he had already gotten himself into.

It was getting late. There was a spit of snow in the cold air mingled with the odors of burning piñon wood. Steve was heartily sick of being confined to his home and the city. He raised his head as he heard the steady tattoo of hoofbeats coming from the direction of the Cerrillos Road. It seemed to whisper to him of the freedom of the open country. Maybe he could get sent to his regiment down at Fort Craig.

The sound of the hoofbeats came closer and closer, and then a horseman swept into the plaza and galloped toward the Governor's Palace. The horseman drew his mount in hard and the big horse reared and flung off. The horseman dropped to the ground. "Where's Major Donaldson, soldier?" he demanded of Steve in a familiar voice.

"Luke! Luke Comfort!" cried out Steve.

The scout bent his head and stared closely at Steve.

"Steve," he said urgently, "where's the major?"

"In the palace, Luke."

Luke brushed past Steve. "What's up, Luke?" asked Steve.

The scout turned and the light from a window fell on his tired face. "It's all over down south," he said tersely. "Three days ago the rebels under Sibley defeated our forces at Valverde. They're advancing up the Rio Grande Valley now. I rode three horses to death gettin' up here. My orders are for all stores in the way of the rebels to be destroyed and for Santa Fe to be evacuated!" The scout passed into the palace.

It was only a matter of an hour before the whole city knew about the disaster at Valverde. Lights glowed in all the houses. Frightened citizens were attacking the hard ground with picks and spades to find hiding places for their money and treasures. Couriers galloped north and east through the cold night to alert all outlying military forces.

Something else beside Luke Comfort had come to Santa Fe. It was *fear,* and it hovered over the city like a dark cloud, whispering in the wind, and the word it whispered oftenest was *deguelo. Deguelo,* "no quarter," for it was said that the *tejanos,* "the Texans," maddened by their losses at Valverde, intended to put Santa Fe to the sword and then burn it to the ground.

Luke Comfort extended his tired feet toward the cheery blaze in the fireplace and looked up at his little audience of Mark and Carter Ames, Steve, and Hernán. He had reported in to the major and had come home with Steve's father and uncle. "The battle," he said at last, "should have been ours, but you know the luck of battles."

They all nodded, and the memory of how Bull Run had turned against the Union forces came back to Steve.

Luke stared into the fire. "We had about four thousand men at Fort Craig, and the rebels had about two thousand.

They were afraid to attack the fort, so they crossed the Rio Grande and advanced north to Valverde. On the morning of the twenty-first our forces left Fort Craig to defend the fords at Valverde.

" We fought back and forth a good part of the day without much result. Then we were to attack their left flank while we held our center with artillery. But, as luck would have it, they decided on practically the same thing. So, while we advanced on the south side of the battlefield, they advanced on the north side of it. The troops we had in support for our artillery were not in position, so the Texans captured our artillery and turned it against us. We had to retreat to Fort Craig. They knew it was too strong to take.

" Canby sent couriers to the north and I was one of them. Some of the boys didn't get through. Anyway, I carried orders that all supplies at Albuquerque, Santa Fe, and Fort Lyon must be destroyed. It looks right bad, gentlemen."

Mark Ames put on his army overcoat and cap. " I'm to leave as soon as possible for Las Vegas," he said, " to rush the Colorado troops and some of the Regulars from Fort Union toward Santa Fe."

Carter Ames nodded. " I'll ride with you, Mark," he said. " The territorial government is to move to Las Vegas and Governor Connelly wants me to go ahead to make arrangements for quarters and so forth there."

Mark Ames looked at his son. " Obviously you're ready for duty, Steve," he said. " Major Donaldson can use you as an orderly here. If the city is evacuated, you are to accompany the troops to Las Vegas. Is that clear? "

" Yes, sir."

When the two brothers had left, Luke Comfort glanced up at Steve. " I didn't mention the fact that we had lost Captain Milas DeWitt at Valverde, Steve."

" No."

Luke stared into the fire with his strange green eyes. " I saw him at the end of the fight. He could have pulled out across the river with the rest of us, but he just stood there near our captured guns, and gave his sword to the first Texan officer he saw."

Luke turned and eyed Steve. " He had plenty of time to get away, Steve. It's my opinion that Milas DeWitt is wearing a new gray uniform right now."

" Amen," said Hernán Calvillo.

Chapter 14

Glorieta Pass, New Mexico Territory,
March, 1862

STEVEN AMES kneed Zouave to the right to pass by the trudging column of infantrymen. They were Germans of Captain Maille's Company finishing their march to Pigeon's Ranch. The smoke of bivouac fires rose in the narrow canyon to mingle with the dust. Supply wagons lined the dusty road for a long distance. It was March 28. There wasn't any doubt that the rebels would soon advance from the city through Glorieta Pass to capture Las Vegas and Fort Union.

Steve had been so busy since the news of the Union defeat at Valverde had come to Santa Fe that he had had little time to think of anything else but his duties. He had been plunged into the type of service he liked with a vengeance. He had been detailed as a courier and spent most of his time in the saddle, delivering dispatches and verbal messages as the Union forces prepared for the next passage of arms that might decide the fate of New Mexico.

There had been fighting and skirmishing in the echoing canyons. News trickled in that the rebels held Carnuel, fifteen miles east of Albuquerque, to hold back any Union force that might attempt to retake the city by way of Tijeras Canyon. Meanwhile, the rebels in Santa Fe had made probing advances toward Johnson's Ranch near Apache Canyon, the entry to Glorieta Pass.

Steve spurred Zouave once he had passed Maille's Company. There should be some units of the Fifth United States Infantry on the road from Las Vegas. Slowly but surely Federal forces had entered Glorieta Pass to plug the hole. There were units of the Third United States Cavalry and the First Colorado Volunteer Infantry, the "Pike's Peakers," who had made a heroic march of one hundred and seventy-two miles through icy winds and falling snow in five days to reach Fort Union.

Somewhere to the south of the pass there was a command of four hundred Union cavalrymen, led by Major Chivington and guided by Lieutenant Colonel Manuel Chaves and Scout Luke Comfort. This command had turned off at San Cristobal Canyon to attempt a wide western swing that would take them to the rear of the rebels who were advancing eastward toward Glorieta Pass.

Steve delivered his message and was about to ride swiftly back to Colonel Slough's headquarters at the ranch when he heard a shrill hail behind him. "*¡Hola, amigo!*"

Steve smiled as he recognized the voice of Hernán Calvillo. Hernán galloped toward Steve on the little sorrel mare that had replaced the long-missing El Diablo. But it was a different Hernán Calvillo from the boy who had left Santa Fe with Steve. He seemed larger and far more imposing, and no wonder, for he was now in the uniform of a drummer boy of militia, with nine rows of white braid set horizontally across his chest, and on his head was a battered Kossuth hat whose wide brim flopped up and down with the motion of the horse.

Hernán drew in his horse, letting it fling off while Hernán doffed his ludicrous hat. "You see before you Hernán Federico Telesfor Donaciano Gaspar Melchior Calvillo!"

"No!" said Steve.

"Drummer in Capitán Rafael Castaneda's Independent Company of New Mexico Provisional Militia!"

" A veteran unit," said Steve suspiciously. " Where are they? "

Hernán grinned. " It so happens, *soldado,* that Capitán Castaneda was promised a commission on the day he signed up his first company member."

Hernán brushed his hat. " *I* am that first member," he said.

" And the *capitán* and his company? "

Hernán looked up at the canyon heights and whistled softly. " I am the *capitán's* company," he said proudly. He eyed Steve. " It is the truth, *amigo!* I am enlisted."

" Has he heard you play the drum? "

" There was really little time, I — "

Steve leaned forward in his saddle. " Has he? "

" Well, no, that is to say, not exactly, I — "

Steve shook his head.

Hernán waved a hand. " No matter," he said grandly. " I have here the dispatch from Las Vegas for the Colonel Slough. Be so kind, *soldado mío,* to tell me where he is."

" At Pigeon's Ranch."

" Then let us be on the way."

They rode together. Hernán glanced at the silver trumpet that hung from Steve's shoulder by its braided silken cord. " You are the trumpeter now? " he asked.

" No."

" Still carrying dispatches? "

" Yes."

They passed the toiling infantrymen. Some of them grinned and made catcalls at Hernán as he rode by in his finery.

Steve waited outside of headquarters until Hernán returned. " Are you going back? " asked Steve.

Hernán grinned. " I told the colonel I was to stay here. I said you had asked for me to help with the dispatches."

" I might have known! "

Hernán shaded his eyes with his hand and looked to the west. " You think there is the chance we will fight here? "

" Not very likely, *amigo*."

Hernán nodded. He looked about. " This is a good time for the siesta."

Steve paid no attention to his friend. He was staring toward two moraines to the west of the ranch, where a cavalry patrol had appeared. They were setting the steel to their mounts. The sun glinted on something in the trees. Dust curled upward from the pounding hoofs of the horses. Then there was a dull, roaring noise from the north moraine, and smoke puffed out into the clear mountain air. Something crashed into the trees near the ranch, and metal tinkled ominously on the hard ground.

The cavalry patrol lay low on their horses' necks as they reached the ranch. " The hills are full of rebels! " yelled the officer who led them.

Steve looked at Hernán as a bugle stuttered into life behind them. " You still going to take your siesta, *amigo?* "

Hernán's face was pale beneath the wide brim of his Kossuth hat. " I think it had better wait, *compañero*."

The next few minutes were a haze to Steve. Orders rattled out like hail on a tin roof as the rebel guns fired steadily at the ranch. But the Union forces moved swiftly into action while Steve, Hernán, and other messengers carried verbal orders to the various Union contingents.

Claflin's howitzers were drawn by galloping horses down the road, scattering yelling and gawking infantrymen. Rebel projectiles plunged through the trees and brush and some of them exploded in cottony puffs on the rutted road. There was a continual slamming noise as the echoes of the artillery guns seemed to bound from one side of the pass to the other.

Robbin's Company of infantrymen double-timed up the road behind the howitzers while Ritter's six-pounder field guns went into battery south of the road, supported by the sweating infantrymen of Sopris' Company.

Colonel Slough stood exposed to the fire of the enemy. He lowered his field glasses and beckoned to Steve. " Tell

Lieutenant Kerber of Maille's Company to take his Germans to the far right flank and try to outflank that rebel battery! "

Thick smoke drifted through the trees as Steve ran toward the Germans. Kerber nodded coolly as he listened to Steve. In a moment he led his men to the right through the trees and then into an irrigation ditch that angled toward the moraine where the rebel battery was in action.

" Look! " yelled an excited officer.

A company of the enemy was double-timing across an enclosed field on the right flank. Steve raced through the trees until he saw Lieutenant Kerber. He yelled and pointed at the Texans.

A crashing volley came from the ditch, and some of the rebels fell while others reached the ditch with ready bayonets. A rebel officer went down. Then Kerber's men appeared at the end of the ditch, and his clear commands rang out. The Germans volleyed three times and drove the Texans back across the field in shattered disorder.

Steve made his way back to the road. Through the drifting smoke he saw Hernán legging it toward a reserve company. Ritter's and Claflin's Batteries roared incessantly and one of the projectiles struck a rebel caisson that blew up with a dull roar and a vivid splash of red flame and white smoke.

Some of the Coloradoans moved to the right to support Kerber. The smoke cleared a little to show the enemy moving against the left flank of the Federals. The Lone Star flag of Texas waved above the rebels. Then volley fire met them from a line of steady Coloradoans and drove them back.

There was a continuous roaring in the air and then came the sound of many hoofs pounding the road, and a unit of mounted Texans raced forward toward Ritter's guns.

" Tell them they must hold! " yelled Colonel Slough to Steve.

Steve darted forward until he was right in the middle of a battery in action. Even as he shouted his message to Captain Ritter the guns belched grapeshot at point-blank range into the enemy and drove them back. The Texans re-formed and came on again. An artilleryman carrying a charge of grape to one of the six-pounders staggered and fell against Steve and then went down forever. Steve snatched up the charge and ran to the gun, and then for the next five minutes he knew nothing else but the deadly and exciting work of a battery of field artillery in close action with a determined enemy.

The guns blasted flame and smoke; blackened swabs plunged into water buckets; the swabs rang against the metal as the bores were cleaned. Powder charges were rammed home; six-pounder grapeshot followed the charges; friction tubes were inserted in the touchholes; gunners stepped free of the wheels, holding the long lanyards in their hands.

" Fire! " yelled Captain Ritter.

The guns spouted flame and smoke, then reared back against their trails. Over and over again until the Texans had had enough. They retreated sullenly to the moraines, leaving many dead and wounded behind.

Steve staggered back from the hot guns. His left shoulder ached intolerably. A blackened gunner sergeant looked at him. " When you get rid of that silver horn you've got there, sonny, you'd better sign up in Ritter's Battery. We can use a good artilleryman like you."

Steve walked back along the road, trying to get a breath of fresh air. Hoofs thudded against the hard earth, and Claflin's Battery came bounding down the slope, through the woods and over the rocks, with a wild-eyed figure hanging on to a caisson with one hand and a battered Kossuth hat with the other. Hernán jumped from the caisson as it passed Steve, rolled over three or four times and came to his feet with his hat at the correct angle. " Claflin and Ritter are to move," said Hernán.

Ritter's guns moved north of the road while Claflin's howitzers joined them. Infantrymen double-timed to support the guns. But the roar of battle had died away, and the smoke was thinning. Men limped toward the ranch houses.

The Texans were moving about in the trees to the right as they massed for another attack. Union officers and noncoms led their men into the woods, where they took up positions among the lichened rocks, and a tense pause seemed to fall over the battlefield.

The Texans came on steadily, with the sun glinting on rifles, bayonets, and swords. Then a hoarse, eerie yelling arose as they increased their pace. Muskets crashed from the Union lines. Smoke billowed out. Cartridges were bitten through and dumped into hot rifle barrels, and ramrods rang as the charges were driven home.

The Texans came on and the Federal lines fell back toward the road. The rebels were after the supply wagons that they could see near the ranch.

Steve looked to the west and saw more of the enemy massing in the road. A bald-headed officer waved his hat atop his raised sword blade.

Ritter and Claflin opened fire, driving back the enemy, but they re-formed and came on again. Again and again the charges came only to be driven back.

Steve plunged through the woods with a message for Lieutenant Kerber. Minie balls whizzed through the trees as Steve relayed his message. Kerber nodded, then his face grew dark. He cupped his hands about his mouth. " Poys! " he roared, " Lay flat dere! Does you vant to go died! "

Steve couldn't help grinning as he went back down the slope. The Texans wiped his grin away quickly enough, for they were forming for the fourth time. Steve reached behind his back and gripped his Sharps, pulling it forward and unsnapping it from its sling. The Texans were trotting toward the guns again. One hundred yards and still the guns were blasting. Fifty yards and the command came to cease firing, while a hoarse yelling arose from the waiting Federal infantry supports. They plunged through the wreathing smoke toward the attacking Texans and met them with a shock.

Steve fired at a Texan color-bearer, but the man did not go down. Suddenly Steve saw that he was separated from his own comrades. A Texan raced through the smoke and fell heavily. A squad of them charged, yelling in that high-pitched tone that sent a chill along the spine.

Steve dropped back looking for his own side and then it was he saw a mounted rebel officer leading a desperate charge against the guns. Steve stared at him. The officer's hat blew off, and he raised the Lone Star flag that he held in his left hand while he fired his pistol with the right hand. It was Milas DeWitt.

A hard hand slammed against Steve's back. " Trumpeter! " yelled a red-faced Union officer, " blow the rally! "

Steve dropped his Sharps and reached for the silver trumpet while the battle raged about him as Texans and Federals fought savagely for the guns. He raised the trumpet to his lips, but there was no chance to blow it. Milas DeWitt had seen Steve. He yanked on the reins of his excited horse and drove it toward Steve. Steve jumped to one side and avoided a savage blow of the officer's pistol barrel. Tripping over a fallen Texan, Steve yanked his Colt from its holster.

Milas DeWitt was fighting with his panicky, rearing horse, and then it turned and raced off through the smoke, with the officer staring back at Steve, hate etched on his face, until the wreathing smoke put a veil between them.

Steve raised the trumpet again and the words of Dacey Curtis came to him above the crash of battle. " Take the silver trumpet, Steve. Don't use it against us rebels. Try to use it to help each othah." He lowered the silver instrument.

The two batteries were being withdrawn by small teams, leaving many dead horses behind them. Kerber's Germans held the raging Texans at bay. The guns went into battery again and took up the battle howl, driving the stubborn Texans back until they were at the far side of the battlefield. It was then that the word passed along the Federal lines to withdraw from the field.

Steve limped back toward the batteries. An angry officer was facing Colonel Slough. "Retreat, sir?" he cried. "We've whipped them!"

Slough's face went taut. "You heard my orders, sir!" He waved a hand toward the distant enemy. "I had no intention of making this a decisive battle. We will withdraw at once!"

The colonel rode from the field followed by hard glances from the sweating, smoke-blackened men. Captain Downing led his men along the road and was stopped by Captain Ritter. "You are the senior officer left on the field," he said. "What are your orders?"

Downing spat. "Double-shot those guns and open fire! I've lost too many good men to stop fighting now!"

A mounted courier came up the road and looked at the angry officers. "Colonel Slough wants to know why his orders have not been complied with," he said.

"Limber up!" roared Ritter. He dashed his hat to the ground and walked away.

Hernán came up beside Steve. "For why do we leave?" he asked. "We have whipped them, *amigo!*"

Steve held out his dirty hands, palms upwards. "*¿Quién sabe?*" he said quietly. "Who knows?"

An ambulance came across the field of battle with a white flag flapping above it. It drew to a halt and an officer got down from it and saluted Captain Downing. "Well, sir?" asked Downing in a sour voice.

"Colonel Scurry, my commanding officer, requests a truce and a cessation of hostilities. May I speak with your commanding officer?"

Downing glanced at Ritter. Ritter pointed along the road to the east. "Colonel Slough is on his way to Koslowski's Ranch," he said. "If you will allow yourself to be blindfolded, you will be led to him."

"That is agreeable, sir."

Downing looked at Steve and Hernán. "Show this gentleman to Colonel Slough's headquarters," he said.

And so it was. Steve and Hernán rode in the back of the ambulance, with their horses tethered behind it, leading the rebel officer to Colonel Slough.

Koslowski's Ranch was a place of much activity in the darkness of the New Mexican night. Lanterns moved from place to place in the hands of medical orderlies and doctors as they took care of the wounded. Off to one side was a long row of the dead, covered by blankets. Wounded men moaned above the sound of the voices of tired men. Smoke drifted about the buildings and through the trees.

Someone shook Steve awake. He looked up into the face of Hernán Calvillo. "I have the good news for you, *amigo,*" said Hernán.

"So?" Steve sat up.

"The Texans will not be back."

"You looked in a crystal ball perhaps?"

"No. Major Chivington and his men have come back. A friend of yours was with them."

"*Sí,* Stevie," a well-remembered voice said from the darkness.

It was Luke Comfort. He squatted beside Steve. "Heard you had a bit of a fracas here."

Steve nodded. "We should have run the rebels all the way back to Santa Fe and beyond."

"Might not have to, son."

Steve sat up. "What do you mean?"

Luke grinned. "I was scouting for Chivington and we heard your artillery fire while we were on the march. When we reached a place called Rock Corral in the rear of the Texan's lines the whole rebel supply train was there with about two hundred of their troops on guard. They opened fire on us with an artillery piece, but we came down from the mountainside in a rush and drove them all off.

"We captured seventy-three loaded wagons, filled with ammunition, forage, clothing, medical supplies, and ordnance materials. We burned those wagons and killed off their whole horse and mule herd." Luke rubbed his hands in enjoyment. "I got a feeling the rebels are going to get a little hungry before long. Come to think of it, I ain't et all day long."

Hernán rummaged in his haversack and lighted a candle. He placed half a roast chicken, some hardtack, and a pot of cold beans before the lean scout. Luke squatted on a rock and began to eat while the boys watched him. When he was done he wiped his mouth. "Delicious," he said. "Well, I guess Colonel Scurry won't get much to eat in Galisteo."

Steve stared at the scout. "What do you mean, Luke?" he asked.

The scout waved a hand. "The Texans are retreating that way. They'll have a long hungry trip to the Rio Grande."

Steve stood up. His mind raced. He well remembered that bulging storehouse in Espectro Valley, not too far from Galisteo. He remembered, too, finding that captain's shoulder strap there and matching it against the other one on Milas DeWitt's blouse in Santa Fe. Then the picture of Milas DeWitt came to him, wearing rebel gray and leading a desperate charge of Texans that very day against the Federal battery.

"What's wrong, Steve?" asked Luke in alarm.

Steve passed a hand across his eyes. He was desperately tired and his mind couldn't seem to function, but he quickly told the scout and Hernán about seeing DeWitt that day, in enemy uniform, and of the stores concealed in Espectro Valley.

Luke stood up. "By heaven," he said in a harsh voice.

" I was always a little skeptical about them stores being there, Steve, but I've never known you to lie yet."

Hernán nodded. " That is so," he said quietly.

Steve paced back and forth. " There were enough stores there to keep the rebels going for quite a while. I know they were there! Flour, beans, bacon, ammunition, medical supplies. Thousands of dollars worth of them."

Luke leaned on his rifle. " Colonel Canby is down at Socorro, a long ways away from the rebels."

" Colonel Slough plans to retreat to Fort Union," said Hernán.

Luke slapped a hand against his thigh. " DeWitt was behind the whole thing," he said bitterly. " Now he's wearing a gray suit and leading rebel charges. It must have been him who side-tracked those supplies for just such an eventuality as this."

They could hear the wounded moaning in the darkness beyond the fires. The wind sighed through the pass.

Steve looked at Luke. " You won't get any troops out of here to capture those supplies if they're still there, and I'll bet they are still there, or close to that place."

" What do we do? "

Steve sat down and pulled on his boots. " Hernán and I know the way. The Texans are tired too. If we can get through the mountains and into the Galisteo Basin before they do, we can set afire those stores and it could be seen for twenty miles."

" Yes! " said Hernán.

Steve buckled on his gun belt and picked up his saddle. " Get the horses, Hernán! If we can set that fire, the Texans will be sure to see it. It will be enough for them to learn something they couldn't be told on a battlefield."

" And what is that? " asked Hernán as he hurried toward the horses.

" That their invasion of New Mexico is over! "

" I'd best report in to headquarters about this," Luke said.

" No time," said Steve. He looked bitterly at the distant building where headquarters was. " Besides, do you think anyone's going to let two boys try a thing like this? "

" No," said Luke. He spat. " Two boys and a man, Steve. Two boys and a man . . ."

They led the saddled horses to the road, then crossed it, and with Luke in the lead, riding as though he had eyes like a cat, they headed for the hulking mountains, which were shrouded in mysterious night shadows. As they rode they heard the sighing of the wind and the distant howling of a coyote. The silver trumpet bumped gently against Steven Ames's back as he rode the big dun.

CHAPTER 15

Espectro Valley, New Mexico Territory, March, 1862

THE MOON hung low to the west of the Galisteo Basin, etching sharply the outline of each tree and patch of brush, making the shadows of the hills and peaks like great pools of ink.

"There is the tower," said Hernán in a low voice.

Luke Comfort stared at it with interest. "The place looks as though no one had been here for decades," he said.

"I know differently," said Steve Ames. He stifled a prodigious yawn.

Luke looked to the west toward the rutted track that led from Galisteo. "Let's go down there," he said.

The two boys followed the lean scout. They had ridden steadily from Glorieta Pass, leading the horses ten minutes in each hour to rest them. There had been no sign of rebels ahead of them or behind them, but they knew there were rebel troops at Galisteo. If one courier got through to Galisteo to warn the troops there of the great loss of supplies at Rock Corral, the Texans would waste no time in getting to the stores at Espectro Valley if they were still stored there.

"It is a place of the dead," said Hernán suddenly.

The bright moonlight shone on the crosses of bright

stones that had been set into the thick walls many years ago. It was almost as though the three people who approached the ancient ruins had left earth by some mysterious process and had blundered onto some long-forgotten and deserted planet.

Luke held up a hand and motioned Hernán to take the three horses off to the right, up a shadowed gully. Hernán swallowed hard, but he did as he had been gestured to do. He turned when he reached the mouth of the gully, and the silvery moonlight shone on the brave white stripes across his coat. Then he was gone.

Luke padded on until he reached the graveyard wall. He stood there a long time with his rifle in his hands, eying each shadow closely. He looked at Steve.

" Beyond the collapsed building," said Steve. " See, you can just make out the roof, close to that great wall of rock there."

" Don't look as though anyone's been here since the turn of the century."

Steve looked behind them, to the west. " I found a copy of an October issue of the Mesilla *Times* here, Luke."

Luke nodded. " Mesilla was secesh then. Like I told you back at Glorieta Pass, I've never known you to lie yet."

They crossed the graveyard and walked past the silent church. Steve glanced sideways as they did so. There was the place where he had fallen with the slug in his shoulder. There was the deep pockmark of Hernán's bullet.

" Lead the way, *amigo*," said Luke. He seemed to be testing the night air with all his senses.

Steve walked to the window by which he had entered the first time. He opened it as he had done so before, with sheath knife and a little skill. He looked back at Luke. " Someone has been here since Hernán and I left in such a hurry," he whispered. " This window was unfastened when we left."

Luke nodded. He jerked his head. " Get back," he said.

Steve shook his head. He eased the window back and put

a long leg into the room, drawing his carbine in after him. In a moment Luke was beside him. The place was cold and evil-smelling.

Steve crossed the room. There was the stub of candle he had left.

Luke spat. "Ain't Jicarillas that used this place anyways," he said quietly.

"How so, Luke?"

Luke picked up a battered tin plate. It was full of fish bones. "No Apache would ever eat fish, Steve. Streams are full of trout, but they don't touch them. It's taboo."

There was a movement in the corner, and Luke dropped the plate and whirled, raising his rifle. An animal scuttled for cover. Luke whistled softly and wiped his face.

Steve pried at the stout door that led into the other room. The door swung back on creaking hinges. Steve poked his carbine barrel inside the room first and then walked inside. There was no sound or sign of life. Luke came in behind Steve. Steve struck a block match and lighted the candle stub. The light flickered up, guttering in the steady draft.

Luke whistled sharply. "This gravels me!" he said.

There was a vast feeling of relief in Steve. The room was much as he had left it, but he was sure there were more stores in it now. The place was literally packed with supplies.

Luke placed a hand on Steve's shoulder. "Thank the good Lord I listened to you," he said. "I only wish some of them back there in Santa Fe had done so long ago. If we hadn't come here this night, and the Texans had gotten ahead of us —"

Steve nodded. "With Canby far south at Socorro and Slough retreating to Fort Union, the rebels have a lot of country to keep under control, providing they have powder and ball."

Luke grinned. "And somethin' to eat. Well, we're here now and we don't need these supplies." He followed Steve along the lines of sacks and boxes until he found the place where the kegs of powder were piled. He whistled softly. "Whoever planned this thing was an expert on supplies."

Steve placed the candle atop a pile of boxes, a good ten feet from the powder cache. "I think we know who planned it," he said quietly. "And he is an expert on supplies, as well as in being a traitor."

"Milas DeWitt."

"Yes."

Luke took a keg from the top of the pile and stove in the head of it with his rifle butt. He picked up the keg and began to lay a thick powder train along the passageway between the rows of supplies. The keg was empty when he reached the door. Luke looked at Steve. "When I get my hands on Milas DeWitt . . ." His voice trailed off.

"Just what *will* yuh do?" a harsh voice asked from behind Luke.

An icy feeling came over Steve. It was too dark down there to see what had happened, but the voice was familiar.

"Come on down here too, sonny," the voice said. "Seems to me yuh would'a learned yore lesson last December when yuh come pokin yore nose in here."

Then Steve knew who it was. The bearded, hook-nosed man who had had that mysterious talk with Milas DeWitt in the middle of the night, the man who had shot Steve through the shoulder.

Steve had left his carbine atop some sacks near the door. He walked toward the door with his heart in his mouth as he felt the gritty gunpowder beneath his boot soles.

There was a strange look on Luke's face as Steve stopped beside him. The yellow light of the candle showed the fierce bearded face of the hook-nosed man, and there was no mercy in the hard eyes. A phrase he had used that night in Galisteo came back to Steve. *Los muertos no hablan.* "The dead do not speak." "To win we have to kill," he had also said.

"Outside," said the man curtly.

Steve followed Luke, but there was no chance to get at his Sharps carbine and he knew the man would never give him a chance to get out his Colt.

" Back against the wall," came the command.

Steve stood beside Luke.

" Raise yore hands! "

They elevated their arms. The man reached inside the doorway and got Luke's rifle and Steve's carbine. He grinned widely, showing uneven yellow teeth. " Two more guns for Sibley's boys. They kin use 'em."

" They'll need them," said Luke. " You rebels can't last. Why don't you give up and go back to Texas?"

" Me? Yuh loco! I ain't no Texican! I ain't nothing but an *hombre* looking for to make a pile of *dinero* out of this war. Let 'em kill each other off. Barney Gaskil is working for profit, not for love of country."

Steve shifted his feet. There was a chance he might get through that window. Where was Hernán?

" What's DeWitt's angle? " asked Luke.

Gaskil grinned. " Same as mine. Only he had to go and make a hero out of hisself by putting on a uniform."

" Two uniforms," said Steve.

Gaskil nodded. " DeWitt was smart enough to stay with the Federals until he saw which way the ball was rolling. He figured he'd lay in a supply of materials for the Texans. It was easy enough to do." Gaskil laughed harshly. " Man, he was right in headquarters! He switched supplies and wagon trains around until no one but me and him knew what was going on. He worked it so the teamsters that drove the wagons were in his pay."

" And the soldiers who were with those twelve wagons last October? " asked Steve.

There was no need for Gaskil to answer. His look was enough. *Los muertos no hablan.*

" So DeWitt stays with us until the rebels win at Valverde, then he deserts the Union and joins the Confederacy," said Luke.

Gaskil nodded. " He believed Sibley would take all of New Mexico."

" But he didn't."

Gaskil shrugged. " The rebels ain't whipped. They're men! With these supplies they can sit tight long enough to get reinforcements. Canby is sitting down at Socorro, figuring Sibley would run out of supplies. I just come from Galisteo. Colonel Scurry knows Colonel Slough has retreated toward Fort Union. Scurry will fall back on Galisteo to get these supplies. After that, well, it looks like Milas DeWitt might'a played the right side after all. Me, I'm in it for the *dinero*." He grinned. " Let 'em all kill each other off. Makes more room for men like me."

" Men? " said Luke softly.

Steve wet his lips. Gaskil had placed the rifle and the carbine near the door to the left of Steve and Luke.

The hook-nosed man's face was set as he came closer to Luke. " You say I ain't a man, *hombre?* "

A new sound came to them above the sighing of the night wind. The steady thudding of many hoofs on the hard-packed earth and the dull rumbling of many wheels.

Gaskil spat at Luke's feet. " That'll be DeWitt," he said, " and the boys from Galisteo for these supplies."

" *¡Alto!* " a sharp voice rang out from outside of the house. The voice of Hernán.

" Good Lord! " said Luke. " The *muchacho* has gone loco. Stopping all them Texicans! "

Barney Gaskil stared at Luke, then started for the door. Steve thrust out a leg and yelled at Luke. Luke was on the big man as he fell over Steve's leg. There was no time to lose. Steve jumped over the two struggling men and ran toward the door of the supply room. He snatched the guttering candle from the mantel over the fireplace and hurled it onto the floor of the supply room. There was a hissing noise as the powder train caught fire. " Get out, Luke! " yelled Steve. He ran toward the outer door. In the flaring light from the other room he saw that Gaskil had

Luke by the throat and was on top of him.

Steve snatched up his carbine, drove the steel-shod butt against Gaskil's head, then dragged Luke to his feet as the bearded man released Luke. Luke and Steve dived through the outer door, Luke snatching up his beloved rifle as he did so.

The area beside the church was full of white tilted wagons and slouch-hatted Texans on their horses. They were but fifty yards from their much-needed supplies, and in front of them was Hernán Calvillo, with presented carbine aimed full at the chest of Milas DeWitt, who sat a gray horse at the head of the Texans.

" *Vámonos,* Hernán! " yelled Luke and Steve in chorus as they leaped the graveyard wall and dropped flat.

" What's goin on heah? " shouted a Texan.

There was a dull, thudding noise and then a tremendous crashing of sound and a huge flare of reddish-yellow light that illuminated the entire valley in a spectral glare. Debris hurtled through the air and smashed against buildings or pattered on the hard earth. Smoke and gas rushed from the explosion and the trees and bushes bent before it.

The great echoes slammed back and forth against the valley walls as though making their way to the Galisteo Basin below.

In the silence that momentarily followed the last sound of the explosion there rose the sound of human voices and that of the frightened horses and mules. Mule teams broke from the control of their teamsters and raced in every direction on the valley floor, followed by yelling Texans trying to master their stampeded horses.

A figure sailed over the wall behind which Luke and Steve crouched and lighted on its skinny haunches. Luke raised his rifle to strike the grotesque figure, but Steve gripped the rifle and forced it upward. " It's Hernán! " cried Steve.

" Let's get out of here," said Luke.

They gripped Hernán under the arms and half dragged

him across the graveyard while pandemonium reigned among the Texans behind them. They darted up the gully to where Hernán had left the horses. One of them was gone, the sorrel mare that had been ridden by Hernán. Luke led the horses up the gully while Steve helped Hernán up behind the mounts.

They did not stop until they were almost at the brim of the valley. Then they looked down toward the old mission. Flames leaped and danced among the buildings and the trees. Most of the white wagon tilts were ablaze too, and in the flickering lights the raging Texans looked like fire-worshipers as they leaped and postured about their precious supplies.

" You see DeWitt? " asked Luke. He raised his rifle and placed a fresh cap on the nipple. " I figure it about two hundred yards range for my old Hawken here." Luke dropped to the ground and thrust the long rifle barrel over a rock.

Hernán spoke for the first time since he had called on the Texans to halt. " Put up your *escopeta,* Luke," he said quietly. " Milas DeWitt will never betray our country again."

They looked at the blackened boy. Hernán wiped the cold sweat from his face. " The blast went over me. Part of the roof struck Capitán DeWitt."

Luke stood up. " You might say he was killed by his own deviltry."

" What do we do now? " asked Steve.

Luke stared down into the valley and then he turned with a grin. " Nothing," he said. " We did what we came to do." He placed a hand on Steve's shoulder. " Only, next time, as a favor to me, Steve, don't time your plans for destruction so closely. You know, for a minute, I didn't think we were going to make it down there."

" Neither did I," said Steve dryly.

" Look at them," said Hernán.

The Texans were rounding up the horses and mules.

But many of the mounts had escaped. Some of them were racing down the valley.

A horse snorted from the brush near the gully.

" There's a mount for you, Hernán," said Steve.

Hernán took a *reata* from Luke's saddle and trotted toward the gully. A horse appeared, etched against the moonlight. Hernán stopped. " It is El Diablo! " he said. " I would know his noble figure anywhere."

" Oh, no! " said Steve.

Hernán dropped the *reata* and ran toward the horse. " *¡Mi bravo! ¡Mi vida! ¡Mi querido amigo!* " He clasped his arms about El Diablo's neck and then turned to take a few steps toward Steve and Luke. It was then that El Diablo swapped ends, laid down his ears, and neatly planted his rear hoofs against the seat of Hernán's trousers, lifting him from the ground and dropping him into a clump of cactus.

There were tears in Luke's eyes as Steve helped Hernán from the cactus. " My brave one! " he said weakly. " My dearest! My dearest friend! "

Hernán stood there in his dignity, wanting to pluck the spines from his flesh but too proud to do so. Then he stalked to his carbine, picked it up, and walked down the slope toward the south.

Luke wiped his eyes. " You told me about that hoss," he said to Steve, " but I would'a never believed it! You think I hurt Hernán's feelings too much? "

Steve shook his head. " I think he expected El Diablo to do that. Seems to be a form of courtesy between them. Where do we go now, Luke? "

Luke scratched his lean jaws. " Best head south. Rebels are to the north and west, between us and our own people. Canby is down south, at Socorro, but the rebels hold Carnuel, which keeps Tijeras Pass closed to us Federals. Best thing we can do, now that the rebels will have to retreat south, is to take to the hills and keep out of sight for a time."

"*Sí,*" agreed Steve.

The scout eyed Steve. "Thanks for saving my life down there, Steve."

Steve waved a hand. "I nearly killed both of us."

They got the three horses and led them south. Far down the slope they could see Hernán Federico Telesfor Donaciano Gaspar Melchior Calvillo limping along in cold dignity. El Diablo whinnied harshly, but Hernán did not turn his head.

Steve was bone-weary. It seemed as though he'd never get enough sleep. But they would have to keep going for a time until they saw the familiar dusty-blue of Federal uniforms somewhere along the great Rio Grande Valley. The war had come to Steve Ames with a vengeance.

The cold moonlight shone with brilliance on the silver trumpet that hung at Steve's back and swung easily at every motion of his body.

Chapter 16

Jornada del Muerto, New Mexico Territory, April, 1862

STEVEN AMES awoke in the darkness of the cave and lay there for some time listening to the night sounds of the Sierra Oscura, the soft sighing of the dry wind and the rustling of the brush, mingled with the dry snoring of Luke Comfort and the rustling of mice in the rear of the shallow cave. It was almost as it had been so many months ago in the Sangre de Cristos when Hernán and he had trailed the lost wagons. He raised his head and looked toward the entrance of the cave and saw the shadowy outline of Hernán's disreputable Kossuth hat.

So much had happened in the time since he had returned to New Mexico. Now he wanted to see his father and his uncle, but that too would take time because a great part of New Mexico was still in turmoil.

The three companions had left the Galisteo Basin and had ridden south, traveling through the mountains by night and hiding by day, keeping away from the trails and roads that led toward the distant Rio Grande Valley. They had learned that the rebels were in slow retreat in the direction of the great valley, with the Union forces under Colonel Canby maneuvering about them. Here and there detached units of both sides moved about the vast country to rejoin their comrades; and mingled with these straggling units were parties of *ladrones* who would rob either side with no compunction whatsoever.

Then there were the Apaches who had taken advantage of the bitter fighting in the territory to strike, raid, loot, and kill almost on the outskirts of the bigger towns. Beyond the guns of the Texans and the Federals, the Apaches held undisputed sway. The smoke of burning ranches, little towns, and wagons stained the clear spring skies every day. It was death for a white man to use the springs and water holes so necessary for life in that arid country, for the Apaches watched them, and if a man was foolish enough to make his camp beside the water, it was the last camp he would ever make this side of heaven.

Luke had led Hernán and Steve to the south, waiting for a chance to get through to the Rio Grande and join Colonel Canby's forces. Time and time again they had had to take wide detours around war parties. They had done without water when they had desperately needed it, to avoid the water hole ambushes. They had done without food because they feared to discharge a weapon. It had been Hernán who had caught rabbits for the three of them by thrusting long strands of thorny brush down into the rabbit holes, then twisting the strands so that the thorns caught in the fur like a hook in a fish, to pull the struggling animals to the surface of the ground.

But now they were without food and with precious little water, and it was only a matter of time before they must strike for the Rio Grande across the northern end of the Jornada del Muerto, the dreaded waterless land that stretched for ninety miles on the eastern side of the Rio Grande, with ranges of harsh, dry mountains blocking the river from the *jornada.*

Hernán shifted. Then he crawled into the cave and placed a hand over Luke's mouth. The boy swallowed hard. "*¡Los indios!*" he said in a dry whisper. "The Apaches!"

Luke and Steve threw aside their blankets and reached for their weapons. The three of them lay down and looked beyond the cave into the shallow canyon below them. It was the time of the false dawn.

For a while they saw and heard nothing, and then there was a movement along the slope fifty yards below them. A line of mounted warriors appeared as though moved by the invisible strings of a master puppeteer. There was no sound from them, for the horses moved on rawhide boots. But there was no mistaking the thick manes of dark hair and the broad deep chests of the Apaches. Now and then, as one of them turned a little, white lines of bottom clay, painted across noses and upper cheeks, could be plainly distinguished against the dark faces.

Fear seemed to float above the silent file of riding warriors, and its grayish-green scum of panic flicked into the cave onto the three whites crouching there.

Steve could feel sweat trickling down his sides and greasing his gunstock beneath his hands, which gripped it so tightly to keep from shaking. Their horses were picketed in a draw a quarter of a mile away. If the wind picked up their scent and carried it to the keen-nosed Apaches or to their mounts . . .

Then the warriors were gone as silently and as mysteriously as they had appeared, and it would have been hard to believe they had been there at all if Steve hadn't known better.

Hernán rested his head on his hands. "I saw the first one fifteen minutes ago," he whispered shakily. "I must have dozed off, because one minute he was not there and the next minute it seemed as though I could reach out and touch him." The boy drew in a deep breath.

The canyon was as quiet as the grave again.

"When he left," continued Hernán, "I was sure it was a dream, until three more of them came along. It was then I woke you."

Luke wet his lips. "No matter how many times you see

'em like that, you never get used to them. I counted thirty of 'em."

" Thirty-two," said Steve.

It was getting lighter. Steve looked past Hernán and he made a quick sign for silence with his free hand.

Another party of warriors was angling down the slope toward the floor of the canyon. There were at least fifteen of them in this party.

" Look! " hissed Luke.

On the far side of the canyon, in the graying light, they could see more warriors dismounting from their horses. The horses were led off and concealed somewhere on the jumbled slope of the canyon wall.

" *¡Dios en cielo!* " said Hernán. " What do they do here? There is no water and no food."

Luke rubbed his bristly jaws. " There is a spring some miles from here, and this canyon is the only way to get there." Luke's strange green eyes looked at the boys. " It's my guess these warriors are preparing an ambush for somebody."

" But who? " asked Hernán.

" What difference does it make? We couldn't do anything about it. Matter of fact, *amigos,* we ain't in such a good situation ourselves. How much water we got, Steve? "

" Why talk about it, Luke? "

" That's what I figured."

" What do we do now, Luke? " asked Hernán.

Luke laughed dryly. " We set and we sweat."

And so it was. They sat and they sweated as the sun came up.

But the Apaches had wasted no time. Those who were at the bottom of the canyon had dug holes along each side of the faintly rutted road. Most of them had crawled into the holes while the rest had covered the holes with blankets and the blankets with earth, so that when the tracks had been erased by dragged brush and the horses had been led off and hidden, there was no sign on that canyon floor that even a lizard had a hole there.

It was the same along the far side of the canyon and to the east end of the canyon. Where before there had been many warriors, now there was nothing but rocks, beginning to change color with the coming of the light, and thorny brush still in the windless air.

The sun rose higher and began to flood the silent canyon with its light, but there was still no sign of the Apaches. They had the patience of spiders.

"Listen," said Hernán suddenly.

The other two raised their heads. Faintly they heard a familiar sound. The thudding of hoofs and the rumbling of wheels, mingled with the popping of whips. A wreath of dust rose up from the east side of the canyon and hung in the still air.

"Now we know," said Luke quietly.

A lone horseman had topped the rise at the eastern entrance to the canyon. He surveyed the seemingly empty place, then raised an arm and pumped it up and down. He rode down toward the canyon floor and in a little while there came a squad of slow riding cavalrymen, wearing slouch hats and gray shell jackets.

"Rebels!" said Luke. "Rebels!"

Half a dozen wagons appeared, with rickety wheels, drawn by weary mules who staggered in their harnesses. Infantrymen slogged alongside the slowly rolling wagons, while behind the last wagon rode another party of cavalrymen, some of them mounted on mules.

Steve took out his uncle's fine German field glasses and focused them on the approaching party. The Texans were thin-faced from lack of food. He scanned the line of wagons and saw men lying in them, with the canvas sides rolled up a little for air. There was no doubt that the men in the wagons were sick and wounded.

"Trying to reach the Rio Grande," said Luke quietly.

"They're in a bad way," said Steve softly. "Those mules

hauling the wagons *might* make the river." He raised the glasses again. " About half of those men have no rifles or pistols."

" Maybe *we* had something to do with *that,*" Luke said.

" But the Apaches! " said Hernán. He looked at Steve with wide eyes. " They will swarm down on them once they are in the middle of the canyon! They will be slaughtered! "

" What do you want us to do? " demanded Luke.

Hernán's face was a mask of horror.

The Texans had no chance whatsoever. They were outnumbered and had the disadvantage of the sick and wounded with them. The Apaches had the vital element of surprise.

There was nothing the three watchers in the cave could do . . . nothing at all.

Steve turned away. It was only a matter of ten or fifteen minutes before those wagons reached the place where the Apaches lay hidden on each side of the road. No one would ever think of looking for them there. When they struck, the warriors on the far canyon wall would also strike. The warriors at the eastern end of the canyon would close in to stopper the bottle.

There was nothing they could do. Steve shifted his carbine and it struck something that seemed to chime like a faint chapel bell. He looked down at the cased silver trumpet.

Luke and Hernán were staring fascinatedly at the approaching Texans.

Steve stripped the cover from the trumpet.

The wind came on a little, carrying with it the steady popping of the whips, the thudding of hoofs and feet, the rumbling and squealing of the ungreased wheels.

Steve stood up. " Luke," he said quickly.

Luke turned. " What's up, Steve? "

" We've got to help them."

" They're rebels! "

" They're human beings, and half of them are sick and wounded."

" He is right," said Hernán. His face was a dirty white.

Luke rubbed his jaw. " All right," he snapped. " But what can we do? "

Steve held out the trumpet. " I'm going to play a concert for those red devils."

" You loco? "

Steve buckled on his gun belt and put on his forage cap. " You and Hernán have a job to do too."

" So? "

" We'll have to get the horses first."

They got their weapons and followed Steve from the cave. It wasn't easy, for they could have been seen by the warriors on the far side of the canyon and the splintered rock and thorny growths played havoc with flesh and clothing, but at last they reached the horses.

Steve swung up on Zouave and looked down at Luke and Hernán. " I'm riding to the west end of the canyon. When you hear me play my first call, I want you to start riding toward the western entrance dragging bundles of brush behind you."

" He is *muy loco!* " said Hernán.

" No," said Luke. He slapped Steve on the leg. " It might work." He looked up at Steve. " If it doesn't, Hernán and I might have a chance to get away."

" I hope you do, Luke."

The scout looked away. " But you won't, Steve."

Steve kneed the dun away from them. He rode swiftly down the slope, angling toward the western end of the small canyon. There was no time for fear. The only fear he had now was that he might not be able to fool the Apaches in time.

He could see the hazy *jornada* to the west as he turned around a great shoulder of rock and looked toward the jagged mouth of the canyon. He drew rein and swung the silver trumpet from his back to his hand. He blew gently into it to warm it, then flourished it. A second later the striking notes of " A Foragers " rang out on the still air and seemed to bounce from the rocky heights above him.

He glanced behind him. Dust was rising high from the broken ground. In a moment it would be seen within the canyon. He spurred the dun forward and lipped into the charge. Again and again he played it as the dust rose higher and thicker, and it seemed to Steven Ames that he was back in Virginia on a blazing July day, listening to a brave Southern boy playing his heart and blood out on the silver trumpet.

The beautiful instrument sounded like a silver bell, like the shrieking of a fierce bird of prey, like the howling of the winter wind among the heights of the Sangre de Cristos. The bright sunlight flashed from the silver trumpet as Steve flourished it, then lipped again into the charge. The silvery notes seemed to lance through the clear air and into the canyon.

Then Steve saw dust rising near the western entrance to the canyon, coming from within the canyon. He slung the trumpet over his shoulder and drew his Sharps forward. He set spurs to Zouave and raced toward where he knew Luke and Hernán would be waiting. The dust was rising higher and faster as he plunged the big dun into a draw.

" Take it easy! " yelled Luke.

Luke and Hernán stood by their sweating horses. Their faces were masks of dust and Steve couldn't help laughing in vast relief.

" Look! " said Hernán.

Steve slid from his sweating dun and raised his carbine.

" No," said Hernán quietly.

The canyon entrance was filled with galloping horses and mules, rumbling wagons, and thick dust. The Texans came tearing down the slope, covered by a handful of their cavalrymen.

There was more dust rising from within the canyon. Toward the eastern entrance it seemed to move faster and faster until at last it faded away in the rising wind of morning.

The Texans drew to a halt fifty yards from the draw. They stared about them in surprise. " Where are they? " asked a lanky infantryman as he clambered down from a wagon.

None of the Texans spoke for a long time as they looked to the west and then to the north and south. There was nothing of human life to see, nothing but the hazy expanse of the Jornada del Muerto, stippled by the fast-moving shadows of high clouds. The mountains were already enveloped in a purple haze.

An officer shoved back his hat and looked at the canyon entrance. " They had us cold in theah," he said. " You men see them devils come up outah thet ground like snakes? "

A big sergeant nodded his head. " We was trapped in theah, suh. They was up on the canyon walls and behind us. They must'a let us walk into thet ambush as neat as yuh please. But wheah is the cavalry we heard out heah? "

" It wouldn't matter if they were our own people or the Yankees," said a red-faced teamster. "Anything is better'n them Apaches."

They sat their horses and looked about them, and then the officer shook his head. " This beats me," he said. He seemed to shiver. " I never did like this country. Always thought it was haunted anyways." He pumped his arm up and down. " No use asking Providence how it saved us. The fact is that it did save us. On to the Rio Grande! "

The column moved out and in time it was nothing but a coil of dust rising from the *jornada,* with now and then the sparkling of metal as the sun struck it.

" What now? " asked Hernán as he mopped the dust from his face.

" I'm thirsty," said Luke.

They led their horses from the draw and mounted them. They rode toward the *jornada,* following the distant Texans.

Twenty minutes passed before Luke spoke. "Why did you do that back there, Steve?"

Steve glanced back toward the low mountains behind them. There was no sign of Apaches. "I made a promise to someone in Virginia last July," he said quietly.

The green eyes were puzzled. "I don't get it, Steve."

"I'll tell you the whole story someday, Luke."

"Yeah."

Hernán smiled. "It is a surety that Steve and I will be of great value to the army now. Myself as a drummer, of course, and Steve with that beautiful trumpet which sounds like a meadowlark beside the canal."

"No," said Steve. "The trumpet will never be played in war again."

"But you are loco!" said Hernán.

Steve shook his head. "It is said that it has magic in it; Jeb Stuart said it would turn a coward into a hero."

Luke nodded. "I believe it."

They rode on and Steve remembered Dacey Curtis. The boy had said war was madness. *"Today you and me fought against each othah and tonight you tried to help me. Take the silver trumpet, Steve. Don't use it against us rebels. Try to use it to help each othah. I don't know how, but I know you'll find a way."*

The silver trumpet would hang on the wall of Steve's home in Santa Fe, near his father's Hawken rifle and above his mother's rosewood piano. Each of them had a story to tell, but the story of the silver trumpet would be the strangest and best of all.

Sources for this Book

STEVEN AMES, his father, Mark, and his uncle, Carter, Hernán Calvillo, Captain Milas DeWitt, Luke Comfort, Steve's comrades in the Eleventh New York Volunteers, as well as many other characters in this story, are fictitious. The boy Dacey Curtis was not a trumpeter with the famed Jeb Stuart, but Jeb Stuart did lead the First Virginia Cavalry at the Battle of Bull Run, or First Manassas, as it was later called by the Confederates. The Civil War custom was for the Union forces to name a battle after the nearest geographical feature, while the Confederates usually named the battle after the nearest town, although by no means was this a strict rule.

The research for THE REBEL TRUMPET was a long and winding trail through many books, letters, and accounts. *Battles and Leaders of the Civil War* (Century, 1887), reprinted by Thomas Yoseloff, Inc., Publisher, in 1957, furnished material about the Battle of Bull Run, the organization of both contending armies at that time, as well as material on the New Mexican Campaign of 1862. *Reveille in Washington,* by Margaret Leech (Harper & Brothers, 1941), gave much interesting information on Washington of early war days and of the various volunteer organizations that thronged to its defense in the stirring spring of 1861.

Turmoil in New Mexico, 1846–1868, by William A. Keleher (Rydal Press, Inc., 1952), gave a wealth of information on the causes and events of the New Mexico Campaign of 1862. *New Mexico,* American Guide Series (Hastings House, Publishers, Inc., revised edition, 1953), was invaluable for its material on the state of New Mexico, its historical information, and the geographical descriptions of portions of the state that appear in THE REBEL TRUMPET. *Texas C.S.A.,* by James Farber (The Jackson Company, 1947), gave much insight into the point of view of the brave Texans who formed Sibley's Brigade in the invasion of New Mexico.

The Look of the Old West, by Foster-Harris, (The Viking Press, Inc., 1955), as always, is invaluable for descriptions of uniforms and other equipment of Civil War times. *New Mexico Historical Review,* published quarterly by the Historical Society of New Mexico and the University of New Mexico (The University Press), contained various articles in many volumes of the series, which were of great value as background material.

Colorado Volunteers in the Civil War, The New Mexico Campaign of 1862, by William Clarke Whitford, D.D., printed by the State Historical and Natural History Society, Denver, Colorado, 1906, provided what is probably the best written descriptions of the battles of Valverde and Glorieta Pass, as well as activities of the Colorado Volunteers and other troops who fought in New Mexico in 1862.

As always, *Official Records of the Union and Confederate Armies* yielded battle and campaign accounts, correspondence of the historical figures who appear in the story, and other excellent background materials. Other books too numerous to mention went into the making of THE REBEL TRUMPET.

A great deal of research was done over a period of ten

or twelve years in the Chicago Public Library, the Newberry Library of Chicago, the library of the Chicago Historical Society, the Los Angeles Public Library, and the Enoch Pratt Free Library of Baltimore, Maryland.

The author traveled through the state of New Mexico a number of times, following the routes of the contending forces, visiting the battlefields and other historical places mentioned in the novel. Special thanks must be given to Miss Leslie Murphey of the School of American Research, the Museum of New Mexico, for the information she forwarded to me during the years of World War II, when I attempted to keep up the research on one war while engaged in another. Her help and encouragement was of inestimable value.

Nothing was of more value in the eventual construction of THE REBEL TRUMPET than the constant help and belief of my wife, Alice, that this book would someday appear in print.

The REBEL TRUMPET

Gordon D. Shirreffs

On a day in April, 1862, young Steven Ames, courier for the Union forces defending New Mexico Territory against Texas Confederates, watches a small military column move slowly toward an Apache ambush awaiting it on the canyon floor below. His friend Hernán Calvillo and the famous scout Luke Comfort watch with him, all three knowing they can do nothing to prevent the impending slaughter. They shouldn't even want to, Luke makes clear. The thin-faced men of the column are rebels.

The dying trumpeter begging Steve for water at Bull Run had been a rebel. At Bull Run, Steve had got his first taste of battle, serving as drummer boy for the New York Fire Zouaves. The rebel had said the beautiful silver trumpet was to be passed from one soldier to another. "Take it, Steve," he said. "Don't use it against us. Try to use it to help each other."

Home in Sante Fe, though, it's the Territory that needs all the help Steve can give. If the Texas invaders capture New Mexico, they'll have the vast military stores at Fort Union and be in a position to arouse Confederate sympathies throughout the Southwest. Such a victory can lead to the North's loss of the Pacific Coast and perhaps of the whole war.

No, it isn't easy to do in New Mexico what the trumpeter asked at Bull Run. Still, the

(*Continued on back flap*)